2000 AD

Sláine

THE HORNED GOD

MANDARIN

Champion of the Goddess

In *Sláine: The Horned God*, our hero arrives fully armoured in his name. Since *Sláine* is Gaelic for health and wholeness, it is a good one for a hero who has so many evils to put right. Wholeness was the prime attribute of Celtic kings, who might not remain in office if they were maimed in battle, a fate which King Rudraige suffers in Book One where he loses his hand in the combat with Avagddu. Anciently, a maimed king could not have congress with the Goddess of the Land. Where there is no marriage between the land and the king, there is war and wasteland.

Sláine's attempt to establish the laws of the Goddess upon a war torn and ideologically confused regime is achieved by his quest for the four gifts of the Goddess. These four holy and empowering objects, called the Hallows, underlie Gaelic tradition and form the mystical regalia of the rightful king. The tests which Sláine has to undergo in order to obtain them, show his fitness to be High King.

The four Hallows derive from the otherworldly cities of Falias, Fineas, Gorias and Murias, according to Celtic tradition, brought hither by the powerful tribe, the *Tuatha de Danaan* or Children of Danu. The Sword of Nuadu of the Silver Hand; the Spear of Lugh, the enabling god of all crafts and skills; the Cauldron of the Dagda, the god who possesses all knowledge; and the Stone of Fal, which is the inauguration stone of the Goddess are all woven into *The Horned God* trilogy in other forms. These empowering gifts represent attunement with the four magical elements of air, fire, water and earth which constitute life itself. Only by proving himself sensitive to these qualities can Sláine become king.

One of the most important factors in this trilogy is the relationship between Sláine and the Goddess, depicted here as the Triple Goddess of the Earth. Feminine aspects of deity have been virtually expunged from our society and been dubbed by philosophers and theologians as mutable, or evil. Unlike the monolithic male Gods of Western culture, the Goddess has many faces and aspects. Like the seasons and the land itself, She changes Her shape, sometimes appearing as the Maiden of Spring, as the Lady of Summer, the Mother of Autumn or as the *Cailleach* (Old One) of Winter. The natural cycle of growth itself – germination, growth, fruition and decay – are reflected in Her many faces. But just as it cannot always be summer, so death and winter also come, and the dark aspect of the Goddess has been needlessly feared. A world without decay is as difficult to contemplate as a world where spring never came.

This acceptance of the cyclicity of life's rhythms is central to Celtic belief. Rather than make statues of their Gods, the Celts preferred to venerate the natural features of hill, stone, tree and river. The old god of nature, Cernnunos, (who becomes Carnun in this trilogy) has become erroneously associated with the Devil, suffering the fate of many pagan deities who were automatically called 'devils' by Christianity. In the royal ritual combat of old king with young *tanaiste* or tribal successor, Sláine overcomes the evil Slough Feg and ends a corrupt era. Our hero proves himself worthy as the Goddess's candidate – a Horned God of great strength, redeeming the dishonour into which the Lord of the Wood has since fallen.

Will Sláine, like his Celtic alter ego, the hero Cuchulainn, have a short life and a glorious? This depends upon those who read and tell his story. A myth lasts as long as the memory of the one who hears and reads it. We have as much need in our times as in the Celtic past for heroic figures who are courageous enough to stand against the evils which beset us. Fortunately, there seem to be no shortage of individuals, whether historical, mythological or fictional, to arise and enter the mould of the heroic archetype and to gladden the hearts of all suffering under injustice and oppression. Before he passes back into the lap of the Goddess, may Sláine live long, reign prosperously and bring Her healing wisdom to all!

Caitlín Matthews

Guide to the Horned God

The Earth Goddess – For the first 200,000 years of human life on Earth a Goddess was worshiped world wide. Only about 5,000 years ago was she gradually replaced by male Gods.

The Triple Goddess – The Goddess could constantly change her form, sometimes 'splitting' into Maiden, Woman and Hag, othertimes Earth, Moon and Sea. Three of her most famous names were Blodeuwedd (Maiden), Morrigu (Woman) and Ceridwen (Hag). The three witches or fates in Macbeth are the Triple Goddess.

The Horned God – The first of her Gods, he is depicted in cave drawings dancing with witches. Worshipped under many names, he was called Cernunnos or Carnun by the Celts. In Christian times he was transformed into the Devil, because of his associations with fertility and nature worship. His cult is still remembered in folk customs such as the Abbots Bromley Horn Dance.

Cave of Beasts – This is based on a great underground cave in the Pyrenees, Les Trois Frères, featuring hundreds of engravings of wild animals and above them a painting of a Horned God. This famous 'Sorcerer' is the basis for The Lord Weird Slough Feg, Sláine's enemy.

The Drune Lords – Led by Slough Feg, they are the enemies of the Tribes of the Earth Goddess. They worship Carnun and Crom-Cruach, the Worm God controlled by the Dark Gods of Cythraul (the Celtic hell).

The Fomors – Sea Demon allies of the Drune Lords, led by Balor of the Evil Eye. Their outpost on Earth was Tory Island off the coast of Northern Ireland.

Warp Spasm – A mystical battle frenzy in which earth energy pours through the body 'warping' the warrior. The Irish Cuchulain is the most famous warped warrior, but other Celtic heroes had similar battle frenzies – King Arthur, for instance, at the Battle of Bath.

Celtic Pronunciation – Sláine: Slaunyeh (although there is another Irish version where it's pronounced 'Slain'); Medb: Maeve; Niamh: Neeve; Tir Nan Og: Cheer Nan Oge.

Cauldron of Blood – A symbol of the Goddess and the original basis of the Grail legend. 'Inexhaustible' cauldrons and huge feasts were a feature of Celtic life.

Ogham Alphabet – Mysterious, Celtic form of writing used by Ukko, one of several versions is given below. It was often written in vertical lines.

| B | L | F | S | N | H | D | T | C | Q | M | G | NG | Z | R | A | O | U | E | I |

LOCHLAN
SEA
DEVILS

ICE SHEET

MIDGARD

BERSERKERS

TRIBES

OF

THE

ERIU

THE
GREAT
MOUND

SESSAIR

ALBION

TITANS

EARTH GODDESS

TITANS

COASTLINE AFTER THE FLOOD

LYONESSE

THE
DOLMEN

TRIBES

OF

THE

CARNAC

DRUNEMETON

DRUNE

GABALA

LORDS

LAND
OF THE
YOUNG
IN
SLAINE'S
TIME

N
W   E
S

CAVE OF
BEASTS

IN A TIME WHERE THERE IS NO TIME,
IN A PLACE WHICH IS NOT A PLACE,
I WRITE.
OF A ONCE GREAT KING, SLÁINE MAC ROTH,
WHO RULED AN EMPIRE THAT WAS NOT AN EMPIRE,
IN A PAST WHICH IS NOT THE PAST,
OR THE FUTURE,
BUT FOREVER.
BECAUSE LEGENDS ARE ETERNAL.

AND IT IS I WHO MUST TELL IT, FOR IT IS I WHO CAN. I, **UKKO THE DWARF**, WHO WAS HIS FRIEND AND COMPANION DURING THE YEARS OF WANDERING THE LAND OF THE YOUNG AND LATER BECAME **THE ROYAL PARASITE** WHEN HE WAS ELECTED KING OF HIS TRIBE.

AS I PAINT THESE WORDS IN MAGICAL OGHAMS ON WAFERS OF BARK, THE MEMORY OF THOSE DAYS COMES FLOODING BACK... OF HIS LAUGHTER FILLING THE ROUND HALL... OF THE CLASH OF HIS MIGHTY WAR AXE "BRAINBITER"... OF HIS HAND SMACKING ME ROUND THE BACK OF THE HEAD...

DAYS THAT CAN NEVER RETURN.

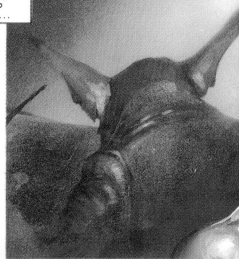

FOR HE IS GONE FROM US NOW.

YET, BEFORE I DESCRIBE THE MOMENTOUS AND TRAGIC EVENTS THAT WERE TO BEFALL THE LAND OF THE YOUNG, I MUST ASK YOU TO BE A LITTLE PATIENT WITH YOUR HUMBLE SCRIVENER...

FOR FIRST, IT IS NECESSARY TO RECALL FOR YOU THOSE INCIDENTS AND CHARACTERS THAT HAVE APPEARED IN MY PREVIOUS TALES WHICH WILL HAVE MORE THAN A PASSING RELEVANCE TO THE ADVENTURE I AM ABOUT TO RELATE...

SUCH DETAILS WILL BE PARTICULARLY ILLUMINATING TO THOSE OF YOU WHO MAY NOT HAVE HAD OCCASION TO PERUSE MY EARLIER MANUSCRIPTS.

SO, CRAVING YOUR INDULGENCE, I SHALL REMIND YOU HOW TIR NAN OG — THE LAND OF THE YOUNG — WAS DIVIDED BETWEEN THE FREE TRIBES OF THE NORTH, WHO WORSHIPPED DANU THE EARTH GODDESS AND LUB THE SUN GOD...

AND THE SOUTHERN TRIBES RULED BY THE DRUNE LORDS, WHO VENERATED CARNUN THE HORNED GOD AND THE BLOODY MAGGOT CROM-CRUACH...

CROM WAS A MONSTROUS TIME WORM — INVISIBLE TO HUMANS — CONTROLLED BY THE DARK GODS OF CYTHRAWL WHO FEED ON THE LIFE FORCE OF MORTALS...

THE DRUNES OFFERED HIM HUMAN SACRIFICES IN GIANT WICKERMAN.

THE SUPREME DRUNE WAS THE LORD WEIRD SLOUGH FEG...

O CROM-CRUACH... GREAT WORM... WELCOME ON THIS SAMAIN'S EVE... THE NIGHT WHEN THE DEAD HAVE THEIR HOLIDAY!

WE OFFER YOU THESE THIEVES, BANDITS AND DREGS OF THE EARTH, WHO— BY THEIR CRIMES— HAVE SHOWN THEY ARE MOST EAGER TO JOIN YOU...

WE KNOW IT'S THEIR SUFFERING WHICH PLEASES YOU MOST!

SLÁINE WAS A MEMBER OF THE NORTHERN TRIBE OF *THE SESSAIR*, BUT HAD BEEN EXILED FOR MAKING LOVE TO THE KING'S CHOSEN ONE, *NIAMH*. JUST SIXTEEN YEARS OLD, HE'D WANDERED SOUTH AND BEEN FORTUNATE ENOUGH TO MEET ME...

IF I EVER GET OUT OF HERE— I'M GOING TO KILL YOU.

I HAD ACCIDENTALLY ALERTED THE DRUNES WE WERE HERE TO RESCUE THE DRUNESS *MEDB* FROM BECOMING *"THE BRIDE OF CROM".*

SLÁINE BROKE OUT AND DRAGGED HER FROM THE HEAD OF THE WICKERMAN...

BUT THE FLAMES FROM THE BONEFIRE BROUGHT ON HIS *WARP SPASM*...

A MYSTICAL *BATTLE FRENZY* WHERE HE COULD WARP THE POWER OF THE EARTH THROUGH HIS BODY...

UNFORTUNATELY, MEDB HAD BEEN SO DRUGGED AND CONDITIONED BY THE DRUNES, SHE'D **WANTED** TO BE SACRIFICED TO CROM AND VOWED REVENGE ON SLÁINE FOR PREVENTING HER BECOMING A GODDESS.

AH, YES, SLÁINE WAS ALWAYS IN TROUBLE WITH THE LADIES! SOON AFTER HE BECAME INVOLVED WITH ANOTHER PRIESTESS— **NEST**. THIS TIME, THOUGH, SHE WAS ON OUR SIDE...

WE WORKED AS LABOURERS ON HER **DRAGON FARM**... WHERE THE YOUNG REPTILES WERE BRED FOR THEIR DIAMOND SKULLS AND JEWELLED EYES...

...BEFORE FLYING ON TO DINAS EMRYS, **THE ETERNAL FORTRESS**, ON **THE KNUCKER**, HER GREAT STUD DRAGON...

THERE, NEW ADVENTURES AWAITED... LEADING TO THE THREE OF US ENTERING OTHER DIMENSIONS AND FACING **THE DARK GODS** THEMSELVES.

AFTERWARDS, NEST STAYED ON AT DINAS EMRYS TO STUDY HIGH MAGIC...

WHILE SLÁINE AND I RETURNED TO HIS TRIBE—HIS LONG YEARS OF EXILE OVER AT LAST.

ON THE WAY HE MET HIS OLD LOVE AGAIN...

NIAMH!

SLÁINE?

AH... NIAMH...! NOT FOR NOTHING DID HER NAME MEAN HEAVEN! SHE WAS A JEWEL BEYOND PRICE... A PERFECT HEIGHT—NOT TOO TALL—WITH LIPS LIKE RED CHERRIES, SKIN WHITE AS...

In Ukko's original ogham manuscript, there then follows a rather personal description of Niamh, dwelling at unnecessary length on her physical characteristics. This has then been crossed through by another neater hand, but is still readable. The identity of this "censor" becomes clear as Ukko's saga continues.

SLÁINE'S REUNION WITH NIAMH WAS NOT A HAPPY ONE... FOR HE LEARNT THEY NOW HAD A SON— *KAI*— WHO SHE WAS TAKING TO THE DRUID SEMINARY AT DURRINGTON...

MY SON... *A DRUID!* OCH, HE SHOULD BE A MIGHTY WARRIOR OF THE EARTH GODDESS!

MY FATHER IS DEAD.

SO IS KAI'S.

GOODBYE, SLÁINE.

SO HE CAN FOLLOW IN HIS FATHER'S FOOTSTEPS AND END UP A CRIMINAL, A DRIFTER AND A TRICKSTER? OR WERE YOU THINKING OF *YOUR* FATHER, ROTH BELLY-SHAKER, A FAT, BOAST-FUL DRUNKARD?

MEANWHILE, IN *MURIAS*— CAPITAL OF SLÁINE'S TRIBE— *KING RAGALL*, SLÁINE'S FOSTER BROTHER, HAD SURRENDERED TO *THE FOMORIANS*...

THE OFFSPRING OF CHAOS AND OLD NIGHT, THESE *SEA DEVILS* WERE ALSO THE ALLIES OF THE DRUNE LORDS...

RAGALL WAS UNDER THE INFLUENCE OF HIS WIFE, MEGRIM... IT WAS THANKS TO HER THE SESSAIR WERE ENSLAVED...

YOU'LL DO WHAT I WANT, RAGALL. YOU CAN'T HELP YOUR-SELF...

IN REALITY, SHE WAS MEDB WHO HAD CHANGED HER APPEARANCE AND BEEN SENT NORTH BY SLOUGH FEG TO CAUSE TROUBLE AMONGST THE NORTHERN TRIBES.

ASHAMED OF WHAT HE'D DONE, RAGALL DECIDED TO GO INTO THE EARTH BEFORE HIS SEVEN YEAR RULE WAS COMPLETE... AND WAS RITUALLY KILLED BY CATHBAD, THE TRIBE'S CHIEF DRUID...

I RETURN TO THY WOMB, O DANU!

FOR A SUN KING, HUSBAND OF THE EARTH GODDESS, MAY ONLY RULE FOR SEVEN YEARS AFTER WHICH HE MUST MERGE WITH HER IN DEATH...

HELLO, UKKO. HOW'S THE LATEST SAGA GOING?

OH... ER... NOT BAD, NEST. NOT BAD.

YOU HAVEN'T BEEN WRITING ANYMORE OF YOUR GRUBBY LITTLE FANTASIES ABOUT NIAMH?

NOT MUCH POINT IF YOU'RE GOING TO KEEP CROSSING THEM OUT.

IS THIS *ALL* YOU'VE DONE SINCE? JUST THESE PAGES...

WELL, WE WRITERS HAVE TO BE IN A CREATIVE MOOD, YOU SEE—

AND YOU'VE COMPLETELY MISSED OUT *THE CAULDRON OF BLOOD!* HOW IT WAS GIVEN TO SLÁINE BY THE EVER-LIVING ONES...

OH, DO I *HAVE* TO GO INTO THAT?

YOU MOST CERTAINLY DO! THE CAULDRON IS CENTRAL TO THE PLOT... IT'S THE LEGENDARY CAULDRON OF *PLENTY... INSPIRATION...* AND *REGENERATION...*

NOT TO MENTION IT BEING THE ENTRANCE TO THE OTHER-WORLD.

WELL, LOOK, I'M AN OLD DWARF NOW, DEAR... I CAN'T KEEP ALL THESE FACTS IN MY HEAD... I GET SO TIRED...

YOU WEREN'T SO TIRED THE OTHER NIGHT, ACCORDING TO THE COMPLAINTS MADE BY THE SACRED MAIDENS OF THE ETERNAL FLAME!

NEHHHHHHH!

NEITHER IS THERE ANY MENTION HERE OF *AVAGDDU*, DISEASED SON OF THE EARTH GODDESS, WHO LIVED INSIDE THE CAULDRON.

NO MORE MEAD— UNTIL YOU'VE COVERED ALL THE POINTS I'VE MENTIONED.

COULDN'T YOU BEAT ME INSTEAD? I THINK I'D PREFER THAT.

YES, RIGHT, WELL, VERY QUICKLY THEN— SLÁINE WAS GIVEN A MAGICAL CAULDRON FOR OUTWITTING THE DARK GODS. THEN ON THE WAY TO HIS TRIBE, AVAGDDU JUMPED OUT OF IT AND SLÁINE HAD A FIGHT WITH HIM. THEN AVAGDDU JUMPED BACK INTO THE CAULDRON.

THEN SLÁINE REACHED MURIAS WHERE HE GAVE HIS STARVING TRIBE FOOD FROM THE CAULDRON.

THEN HE HAD A WARP SPASM, KILLED SOME FOMORIANS, AND WAS ELECTED KING IN RAGALL'S PLACE.

CAN I HAVE THAT MEAD NOW?

SLÁINE HAD BECOME KING AT A TIME OF GREAT PERIL FOR THE TRIBES OF THE EARTH GODDESS... AT *CARNAC*, TO THE SOUTH, *THE LORD WEIRD SLOUGH FEG* ORDERED LONG AVENUES OF *WEIRD STONES* TO BE ERECTED THAT SENT POWER SEETHING THROUGH MAGICAL LEY LINES...

DRAGGING DOWN A GREAT SHEET OF ICE OVER THE LAND OF THE YOUNG...

AND WITH GLACIERS CAME THE DRUNES' FOMORIAN ALLIES IN GREAT *"TOWERS OF GLASS"*, LED BY *BALOR OF THE EVIL EYE* WHOSE HIDEOUS GAZE BURNED ALL WHO CAME BEFORE IT.

BUT, INVIGORATED BY THE FOOD FROM THE MAGICAL CAULDRON, SLAINE'S TRIBE FOUND NEW HOPE AND FOUGHT OFF THE SEA DEVILS...

SOME EVEN CHARGING INTO BATTLE "SKY CLAD" SO THEY COULD DRAW ON THE MAGICAL POWER OF THE GODDESS DANU...

WHO WATCHED ABOVE THE BATTLE IN HER THREE ASPECTS OF MAIDEN... WOMAN... AND HAG... BLODEUWEDD, LADY OF THE FLOWERS... MORRIGU, CROW OF WAR... AND CERIDWEN, MOTHER OF DEATH...

THE THOUGHT OF THE EARTH—HIS WIFE—BEING DEFILED BY THE MONSTERS FROM THE DEEP BROUGHT ON SLÁINE'S **WARP SPASM**...TURNING HIM INTO A RAGING BEAST...

COMPLETELY BERSERK, HE RUSHED FORWARD INTO THE RANKS OF THE ENEMY, MOWING DOWN GREAT SWATHES OF THEM WITH HIS AXE "BRAINBITER". HE DID NOT SLACKEN HIS ONSLAUGHT UNTIL HE HAD KILLED FOUR HUNDRED AND SEVENTY FOMORS. HE DIDN'T THINK IT TOO MANY.

IN FACT, HE DIDN'T THINK IT ENOUGH. FOR SO VAST WERE THE FOMORIANS' NUMBERS, ONE TRIBE ALONE COULD NOT DESTROY THEM. IT WOULD BE NECESSARY FOR THE SESSAIR TO FORM AN **ALLIANCE** WITH THE OTHER TRIBES OF THE EARTH GODDESS...

BUT SLÁINE'S PROPOSAL MET WITH FIERCE OPPOSITION FROM WITHIN HIS TRIBE, FOR—ABOVE ALL—CELTS VALUE **FREEDOM** AND DESPISE AND FEAR **EMPIRES**, REGARDING THEM AS A BARBARIC AND UNCIVILISED NOTION THAT WILL INEVITABLY LEAD TO DICTATORSHIP AND MISERY...

I SEE NO SHAME IN ADMITTING I HAVE AMBITIONS.

SIRE, THEY ARE *THE FORBIDDEN WEAPONS* FROM ATLANTIS... SUCH WEAPONS CAUSED A *TERRIBLE WAR* IN THAT ONCE GREAT LAND, RESULTING IN IT SINKING BENEATH THE WAVES...

...WOULD YOU RISK TIR NAN OG SHARING ITS FATE?

WITH MAGICAL WEAPONS LIKE THE SPEAR AND THE SWORD I COULD PUT AN END TO WAR.

OHO! HOW MANY RULERS HAVE THOUGHT WONDER *WEAPONS* WERE THE ANSWER TO ALL THEIR PROBLEMS..? AND HOW OFTEN DID THEY LEAD TO THEIR END?

WE DON'T HAVE ANY ALTERNATIVE!

PRAYER IS THE ALTERNATIVE, MY BOY. WE MUST PRAY... TO THE TRINITY OF *HU THE MIGHTY, LUG THE SUN GOD* AND *DANU THE EARTH GODDESS* FOR DELIVERANCE.

PUT YOUR FAITH IN THEM AND YOU WILL BE REWARDED... IF NOT IN THIS WORLD, IN THE NEXT.

WHAT ABOUT PEOPLE SUFFERING *NOW?*

SUFFERING IS *GOOD* FOR THEM. YOU KNOW, WHEN HUMAN BEINGS ARE IN ADVERSITY, THAT'S WHEN THEIR GOOD QUALITIES REALLY COME OUT.

YOU DARE TO DEFY YOUR DRUID, BOY! I AM THE HIGHEST AUTHORITY IN THE LAND—ABOVE EVEN THE KING!

BUT THERE IS ONE ABOVE EVEN YOU, CATHBAD... *THE GODDESS HERSELF.*

I SHALL CONSULT *HER* ON THIS MATTER... BY ENTERING THE CAULDRON OF BLOOD!

I WAS NOT PRESENT DURING THE ARGUMENT (ALTHOUGH I HEARD ABOUT IT LATER) ON ACCOUNT OF SOME OVER-INDULGING AT THE *VICTORY FEAST*... WHICH RESULTED—IF I MAY BE SO INDELICATE—IN MY SPENDING A CONSIDERABLE TIME IN THE TRIBAL LATRINES...WHERE I HAPPENED TO BE AS MEGRIM PASSED BY...

DWARF! COME HERE!

YES, MY LADY?

I MUST VISIT THE LORD WEIRD. GO TO THE FOREST RENDEZVOUS AND PREPARE MY BOWLS AND HERBS.

I SHALL JUST HAVE TO SEE WHAT THE EARTH GODDESS HAS TO SAY ABOUT *THE HORNED GOD*, CATHBAD.

I...I REALLY DON'T THINK THAT'S A GOOD IDEA, SIRE.

IT COULDN'T BE YOU *DRUIDS* HAVE BEEN TWISTING RELIGION *AS WELL AS THE DRUNES?*

WHY NOT?

OF COURSE NOT, SIRE! *THE VERY IDEA!*

AS SLÁINE DESCENDED INTO THE CAULDRON, HE NOTICED THE FIGURE ON THE INSIDE WAS *CARNUN*... SURROUNDED BY HIS ANIMALS...

BUT, DESPITE CATHBAD'S GRIM WARNINGS, THE SIGHT OF THE LORD OF THE BEASTS, DIDN'T FILL HIM WITH DREAD AND FOREBODING. RATHER, IT REASSURED HIM...

FOR CARNUN HELD IN ONE HAND *THE EARTH SERPENT*, A SYMBOL OF THE GODDESS HERSELF.

AND THE GOD'S NON-THREATENING POSE CONFIRMED HIS OWN INSTINCTIVE FEELING THAT JUST BECAUSE CARNUN WAS WORSHIPPED BY HIS ENEMIES, DIDN'T MEAN HE WAS NECESSARILY EVIL.

IN FACT, HE WAS CURIOUS TO KNOW MORE ABOUT HIM AND HIS MYSTERIOUS CONNECTION WITH THE TREASURES OF DANU HE NEEDED SO DESPERATELY.

HARDLY HAD THESE THOUGHTS BUBBLED INTO HIS CONSCIOUSNESS WHEN HE HEARD A FEMALE VOICE, INSIDE HIS HEAD, CALLING HIM...

SLÁINE...

AND HIS HEART LEAPT AND A SHIVER OF FEAR AND EXCITEMENT RAN DOWN HIS SPINE FOR HE KNEW IT WAS THE GODDESS HERSELF.

"YOU HAVE TAKEN THE FIRST STEPS IN SEEKING MY ADVICE... IN QUESTIONING THE WORLD YOU LIVE IN AND ITS VALUES...

NOT ACCEPTING THEM WITH BLIND FAITH."

"IN YOUR ADVENTURES YOU HAVE OFTEN STOOD ON THE EDGE OF THE SEA OF AWARENESS, BUT WERE TOO AFRAID TO ENTER...

"NOW IT IS TIME. COME..."

"RECEIVE THE HIDDEN KNOWLEDGE THAT HAS MANY NAMES, BUT YOU CALL THE CAULDRON OF WISDOM... OR GRAIL...

"THE KNOWLEDGE MEN SEEK FAR AND WIDE...

"BUT IS INSIDE THEM ALL THE TIME..."

"...SUBMERGED DEEP WITHIN THEIR SUBCONSCIOUS."

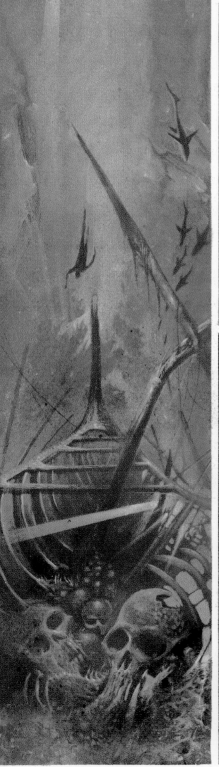

"RACE MEMORIES OF A BYGONE ERA WHEN, FOR TWO HUNDRED THOUSAND YEARS, MEN WORSHIPPED A GODDESS AND THERE WERE NO GODS..."

"AN ERA WHEN WOMEN LOOKED AFTER THE EARTH."

"AN ERA MEN HAVE CONVENIENTLY CHOSEN TO FORGET OR DENY... YET SECRETLY YEARN TO RETURN TO, EVEN THOUGH THEY DREAD IT..."

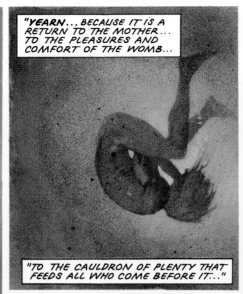

"YEARN... BECAUSE IT IS A RETURN TO THE MOTHER... TO THE PLEASURES AND COMFORT OF THE WOMB..."

"TO THE CAULDRON OF PLENTY THAT FEEDS ALL WHO COME BEFORE IT..."

"DREAD... BECAUSE IT IS ALSO A RETURN TO THE BLACK, BOTTOMLESS PIT OF THE UNKNOWN FROM WHICH THEY SPRANG..."

"WHEN THEY WERE POWERLESS, ALONE AND AFRAID..."

"BUT FIRST THEY MUST DEFEAT THE SEA DEMONS WHO DWELL THERE..."

"...MATERIALISATIONS OF THEIR FEARS OF RETURNING TO THE LOST ERA OF WOMEN."

"TO DEFEAT THEM, YOU HAVE TO ACCEPT THIS KNOWLEDGE AND BE PREPARED TO REJECT THE MALE PATH OF POWER AND DOMINATION OVER WOMEN.

"ONLY WHEN YOU HAVE OVERCOME YOUR MENTAL DEMONS WILL YOU BE READY FOR WHAT LIES BEYOND."

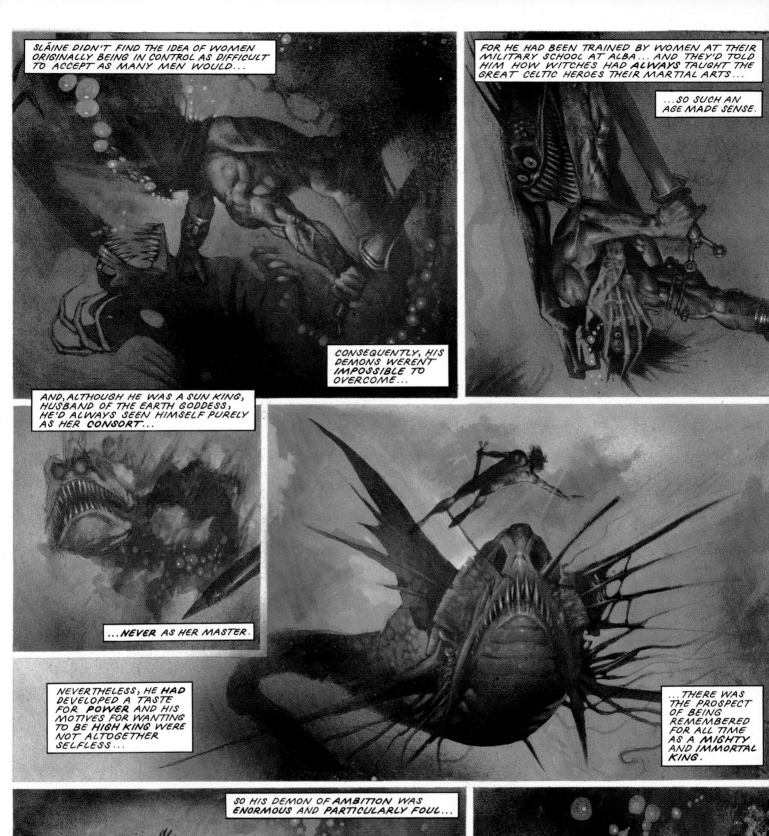

SLÁINE DIDN'T FIND THE IDEA OF WOMEN ORIGINALLY BEING IN CONTROL AS DIFFICULT TO ACCEPT AS MANY MEN WOULD...

FOR HE HAD BEEN TRAINED BY WOMEN AT THEIR MILITARY SCHOOL AT ALBA... AND THEY'D TOLD HIM HOW WITCHES HAD ALWAYS TAUGHT THE GREAT CELTIC HEROES THEIR MARTIAL ARTS...

...SO SUCH AN AGE MADE SENSE.

CONSEQUENTLY, HIS DEMONS WEREN'T IMPOSSIBLE TO OVERCOME...

AND, ALTHOUGH HE WAS A SUN KING, HUSBAND OF THE EARTH GODDESS, HE'D ALWAYS SEEN HIMSELF PURELY AS HER CONSORT...

...NEVER AS HER MASTER.

NEVERTHELESS, HE HAD DEVELOPED A TASTE FOR POWER AND HIS MOTIVES FOR WANTING TO BE HIGH KING WERE NOT ALTOGETHER SELFLESS...

...THERE WAS THE PROSPECT OF BEING REMEMBERED FOR ALL TIME AS A MIGHTY AND IMMORTAL KING.

SO HIS DEMON OF AMBITION WAS ENORMOUS AND PARTICULARLY FOUL...

AND IT WAS SOME TIME BEFORE HE VERY RELUCTANTLY FINISHED IT...

AND WAS READY FOR WHAT LAY BEYOND.

GODDESS!

SO WHY ARE YOU HERE, MORTAL? WHY HAVE YOU VISITED ME IN MY SECRET CAVE?

TO SEEK YOUR PERMISSION TO GO IN SEARCH OF YOUR TREASURES.

"TO GO IN SEARCH OF YOUR TREASURES".

WELL, AT LEAST HE ASKED!

THAT'S MORE THAN SOME! THEY'LL JUST TRY AND GRAB THEM!

AND ARE YOU READY TO PAY THE PRICE?

YES— WILL YOU PAY THE PRICE?

I THOUGHT I'D SHOWN I WAS.

YOU ARE PREPARED TO FOLLOW *THE WAY OF THE HORNED GOD?*

I SUPPOSE SO... ALTHOUGH I'M NOT SURE WHAT THE HORNED GOD IS... SO... IT DEPENDS...

CARNUN—AS YOU CELTS CALL HIM—IS THE GOD OF NATURE... OF FERTILITY... *THE FIRST OF MY GODS...*

THE ONLY ONE WHO NEVER BETRAYED ME.

WHICH IS PROBABLY WHY SOME CALL HIM THE DEVIL.

HE SEES THE RIDICULOUSNESS OF LIFE. HE NEVER TAKES ITS PRESSURES TOO SERIOUSLY. HE SEES THE LAUGH OF IT ALL. HE SEES THE GAME FOR WHAT IT IS.

HE IS THE LAUGHTER IN THE WOODS.

WHEREAS THE SUN GOD IS SO *SERIOUS...* IS OBSESSED WITH *AUTHORITY...* WITH *CONQUERING* EVERYTHING... THOSE HEROES WHO FOLLOW HIS PATH ARE USUALLY *MINDLESS* AND *VIOLENT...*

STILL, YOU DID LEAVE YOUR TRIBE WHEN YOU WERE SIXTEEN AND STILL VERY IMMATURE... AND MEETING UP WITH THAT *AWFUL DWARF* WAS PROBABLY THE WORST THING THAT COULD HAVE HAPPENED TO YOU.

Note: In the original ogham manuscript, the writing is much neater here and there are none of the usual crossings-out and stains. This would suggest this chapter has actually been written by Nest rather than Ukko. Elsewhere in the saga, also, there are indications she may have rewritten Ukko's sometimes coarse version of events or told him what to write.

I THINK YOU'RE BEING RATHER HARD ON *SUNHEROES*. AFTER ALL, WE ARE YOUR EARTHLY HUSBANDS AND OUR TRIBES ARE NAMED AFTER YOU.

BULLDUNG! YOUR DRUIDS PAY ME LIP SERVICE. THEY PUT ME ON A PEDESTAL WHERE I'M OUT OF THE WAY AND NO LONGER A "THREAT". THEN TRY TO CONTROL ME BY PUTTING MALE GODS OVER ME.

ONLY THE HORNED GOD IS STILL SUBORDINATE TO ME. HE UNDERSTANDS HIS POSITION.

HE IS THE MALE REPRESENTATIVE OF LIFE. MY ARM. BUT HE IS NOT AFRAID OF DEATH... OF LOSING CONTROL... BECAUSE HE KNOWS IT'S ONLY A RETURN TO ME...

HE KNOWS IT'S ALL A GAME. MY SPORT. BECAUSE THAT'S HOW NATURE IS...

"HE IS THE JOY OF LIFE... THE LAUGHTER IN THE WOODS..."

PONDERING ON WHAT HE HAD LEARNT, SLAINE REASCENDED INTO THE LAND OF THE LIVING...

THE REVELATION THAT **THE HORNED GOD** WAS NOT A DEVIL AS CATHBAD HAD CLAIMED HAD NOT COME AS ANY GREAT SURPRISE TO HIM...

PERHAPS BECAUSE AS A YOUTH, HE'D LEFT HIS TRIBE AND ITS NARROW RELIGIOUS TEACHINGS AND WANDERED AMONGST THE SOUTHERN TRIBES WHERE **CARNUN** WAS WORSHIPPED...

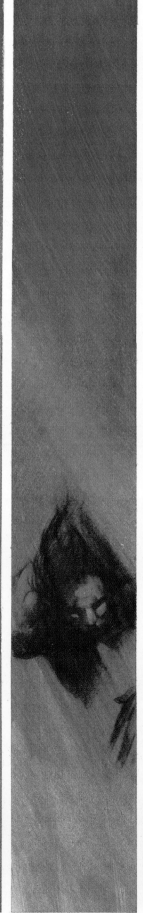

...AND SEEN FOR HIMSELF THAT HE WAS A GOD OF **LAUGHTER**... AND **DANCING**... AND **FERTILITY**... HARDLY A DEMON, UNLESS YOU HAPPENED TO DISAPPROVE OF MAKING MERRY...

NOR HAD HE FELT **THREATENED** BY THE GODDESS AND HER INEXHAUSTIBLE CAULDRON...

...THE KNOWLEDGE THAT NO MATTER HOW FIERCELY OR PASSIONATELY HE LOVED HER, THERE WOULD BE A DISTANCE BETWEEN THEM THAT WOULD MAKE HIM HUNGRY...

AN EMPTINESS HE COULD NEVER SOMEHOW FILL.

THAT NO MATTER HOW BRIGHT HIS PLUMAGE, HOW SPIKY HIS HAIR, HOW POWERFUL AND HANDSOME HE WAS, SHE COULD STILL SWALLOW HIM.

THE GODDESS, NOT HER GODS, WAS IN CONTROL.

THIS WAS **THE GREAT SECRET** HEROES SOUGHT ON THEIR QUESTS...

BUT IT WAS NO OCCULT TRUTH, JEALOUSLY GUARDED BY SOME ELITE ORDER OF HIGH PRIESTS...

EVERYONE KNEW IT ALL ALONG.

THEY'D JUST FORGOTTEN IT.

MEANWHILE, YOUR HUMBLE SCRIVENER HAD FOLLOWED MEGRIM'S DWARF, **ROBYM**, TO A SECRET SPOT IN THE FOREST WHERE HE WAS JOINED BY HIS MISTRESS...

I WATCHED AS SHE HEATED UP STRANGE CONCOCTIONS IN SEVEN BOWLS MADE FROM YEW, WALNUT, HAZEL, APPLE, ALDER, WILLOW AND BEECH...

INHALING THEIR COMBINED VAPOURS...

AS MEGRIM FLOATED THROUGH THE MISTS OF TIME AND SPACE, SHE DREAMILY RECALLED HER PAST... WHEN SHE WAS KNOWN AS MEDB...

HOW AS A CHILD, SHE WAS TAKEN FROM HER VILLAGE BY THE SKULL SWORDS TO BE OFFERED UP TO THE LORD WEIRD SLOUGH FEG IN HIS CAVE OF BEASTS, DEEP WITHIN THE EARTH...

(Ukko did not follow Megrim, but probably with help from Nest — he speculates on what she was thinking and her destination... based on his knowledge of the final outcome of events.)

AND SO HE HAD SPARED HER LIFE... MAKING HER A PRIESTESS OF HIS DEATH CULT... WHOSE CHIEF DEITY WAS CROM-CRUACH, THE MAGGOT GOD...

TEACHING HER THAT BECAUSE LIFE ON THIS EARTH IS FULL OF MISERY AND SORROW, WE MUST THANK CROM FOR THE GIFTS OF WAR, DISEASE AND DISASTER THAT WILL PUT AN END TO IT.

BUT WHILE THE OTHER VICTIMS HAD SOBBED AND TREMBLED IN THE PRESENCE OF THE LORD WEIRD, SHE HAD NEVER CRIED OUT WHEN IT WAS HER TURN...

IN FACT, HE HADN'T NEEDED TO TEACH HER ANYTHING... MERELY GIVE SHAPE AND FORM TO HER OWN THOUGHTS AND FANTASIES...

FOR, AS LONG AS SHE COULD REMEMBER, SHE'D BEEN FASCINATED BY THE DESTRUCTIVE SIDE OF NATURE...

THE SUDDEN FURY OF A WINTER BLIZZARD, KILLING CROPS AND CATTLE OVERNIGHT... THE SAVAGERY OF THE OCEAN, SMASHING HELPLESS SHIPS AGAINST THE ROCKS...

DEATH WAS FAR MORE EXCITING THAN LIFE...

THE DARK SIDE OF THE GODDESS... UNINHIBITED, WILD... HOWLING AT THE MOON... AND ALL-DEVOURING WAS IN HER.

BUT SHE SAW NO CONTRADICTION IN BEING AGAINST **THE TRIBES** OF THE EARTH GODDESS... FOR THEIR VIEW OF NATURE WAS AS A GIGANTIC EARTH MOTHER PRODUCING CHILDREN TO THE ORDER OF HER HUSBAND THE SUN GOD...

OR AN INNOCENT, EMPTY-HEADED, PRETTY MAIDEN, PLACID AND SUBMISSIVE...

NOT THAT WAY FOR MEDB!

NATURE ITSELF, AFTER ALL, WAS CONTRADICTORY... CONSTANTLY CHANGING... ONE DAY BLOOMING WITH LIFE, THE NEXT DARK AND SINISTER...

...SO SHE'D HAD NO DIFFICULTY IN RECONCILING HERSELF TO BECOMING THE BRIDE OF THE GREAT WORM... SHE THE GODDESS, THE QUICKENER—BEARING THE SEED OF DEATH—IN A CEREMONY THAT WAS A GROTESQUE INVERSION OF LIFE.

BUT SHE'D BEEN CHEATED OF THAT HONOUR, THANKS TO SLÁINE.

AND NOW, AFTER ALL THIS TIME, SHE'D MET UP WITH HIM AGAIN... AND ONCE MORE HE'D INTERFERED...

...PREVENTING HER BEING ELECTED QUEEN OF THE SESSAIR, AFTER HER HUSBAND HAD KILLED HIMSELF.

WORSE, SLÁINE'S PLAN TO UNITE THE TRIBES OF THE EARTH GODDESS, COULD RUIN SLOUGH FEG'S CAREFULLY LAID PLANS FOR THE DESTRUCTION OF THE LAND OF THE YOUNG.

SHE MUST REPORT TO HER LORD...

MEDB SCANNED THE CAVE OF BEASTS FOR HIM...

HER EYE TAKING IN THE SINGLE **PAINTING** OF HIM AMONGST THE HUNDREDS OF ANIMALS BEAUTIFULLY **ENGRAVED** ON THE WALL...

...A SELF-PORTRAIT OF HIM WHEN HE WAS YOUNG AND VIRILE AND DANCED WITH HIS COVEN IN THE LOST AGE OF WITCHES.

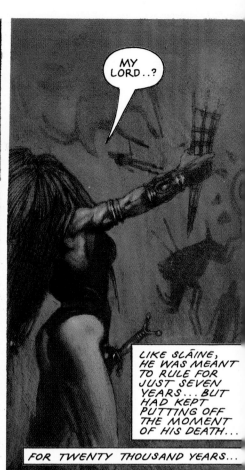

MY LORD..?

LIKE SLÁINE, HE WAS MEANT TO RULE FOR JUST SEVEN YEARS...BUT HAD KEPT PUTTING OFF THE MOMENT OF HIS DEATH...

FOR TWENTY THOUSAND YEARS...

KEEPING HIMSELF "ALIVE" BY FEEDING ON THE GREAT WORM'S EGGS...MEDB COULD HEAR HIM NOW...GIBBERING TO HIMSELF IN THE DARK...

MY LORD..?

...BUT IT WAS HIS **SMELL**—HIS "MYSTIC AURA"—THAT DREW HER TO THE SPOT WHERE SHE FOUND...

...WORKING ENTIRELY IN THE DARK ON ANOTHER OF HIS MASTERPIECES, DRIBBLING, STINKING, UTTERLY INSANE...THE LORD WEIRD SLOUGH FEG...

THE OLD HORNED GOD.

DESPITE HIS INSANITY—OR PERHAPS BECAUSE OF IT—FEG WAS A BRILLIANT ARTIST. WITH OWL-LIKE EYES PIERCING THE DARKNESS, HE COMMEMORATED THE **JOY OF THE HUNT** IN HIS MAGICAL DRAWINGS...

...BELIEVING AN ANIMAL'S SPIRIT IS NOT OFFENDED BY BEING KILLED, FOR **FOOD**... PROVIDED IT IS PAID TRIBUTE.

OVER THE CENTURIES, HE DEVELOPED THIS BELIEF INTO A DEATH CULT—TO JUSTIFY THE SLAUGHTER OF HUMANS...

...WHO WERE KILLED IN DELIBERATELY INSTIGATED WARS TO PROVIDE **FOOD** FOR THE DARK GODS HE WORSHIPPED.

TO THESE MONSTERS FROM **CYTHRAUL**—OR HELL—HUMANS WERE JUST ANOTHER SPECIES OF ANIMAL...

...AND **WARS**, ARRANGED AT SUITABLE INTERVALS TO ALLOW NEW GENERATIONS TO GROW AND "RIPEN", WERE THE MOST CONVENIENT WAY TO "HARVEST" THE CROP...

...THEIR LIFE ESSENCE SUCKED BACK TO CYTHRAUL THROUGH THE GREAT WORM, CROM-CRUACH.

BUT, REGARDING HIMSELF AS **LORD OF THE ANIMALS**, FEG POSTPONED HIS OWN END INDEFINITELY... AND PAID A TERRIBLE PRICE...

ROTTING AND INSANE...

IMPOTENT AS THE SOUL LAND HE RULED OVER.

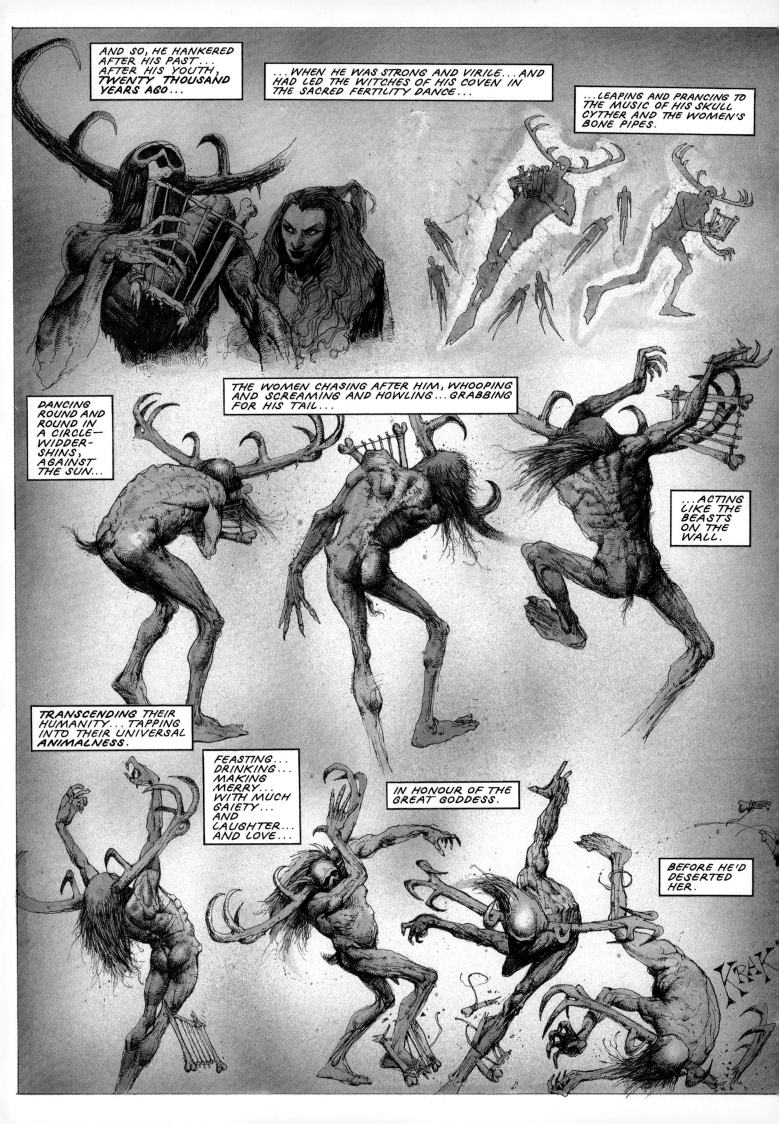

AND SO, HE HANKERED AFTER HIS PAST... AFTER HIS YOUTH, TWENTY THOUSAND YEARS AGO...

...WHEN HE WAS STRONG AND VIRILE...AND HAD LED THE WITCHES OF HIS COVEN IN THE SACRED FERTILITY DANCE...

...LEAPING AND PRANCING TO THE MUSIC OF HIS SKULL CYTHER AND THE WOMEN'S BONE PIPES.

THE WOMEN CHASING AFTER HIM, WHOOPING AND SCREAMING AND HOWLING...GRABBING FOR HIS TAIL...

DANCING ROUND AND ROUND IN A CIRCLE— WIDDER-SHINS, AGAINST THE SUN...

...ACTING LIKE THE BEASTS ON THE WALL.

TRANSCENDING THEIR HUMANITY...TAPPING INTO THEIR UNIVERSAL ANIMALNESS.

FEASTING... DRINKING... MAKING MERRY... WITH MUCH GAIETY... AND LAUGHTER... AND LOVE...

IN HONOUR OF THE GREAT GODDESS.

BEFORE HE'D DESERTED HER.

KRAK

MY LORD WEIRD!

NOW HE NO LONGER HAD ANY ZEST FOR LOVE...FOR LIFE...AND HE BLAMED THE GODDESS FOR IT: HATED HER FOR IT.

HATED ANYTHING TO DO WITH LIFE. TOOK PLEASURE ONLY IN DEATH.

HERE... THIS WILL REVIVE YOU.

REVERTING TO THE CURIOUS SYNTAX OF HIS YOUTH, HE SPOKE OF HIS PAST...IN SINISTER, YET BIRD-LIKE TONES, ALMOST SINGING THE WORDS...

IN SPLENDID ORDER WE DANCED, MEDB... REVELLING IN WINE FROM THE HORN. NOT SCANTY WAS THE FEAST...HIGHLY CONGENIAL TO ME WERE THOSE DAYS.

I WISH I'D BEEN A YOUNG WITCH THEN...AND DANCED WITH YOU IN THIS SACRED PLACE...

BEFORE YOU GREW OLD.

AYE...BUT NOW ALL I WISH FOR IS THE REPOSE OF DEATH...THE WOMB OF WHICH IS FILLED WITH DEEP INTEREST FOR ME. IT ALLURES ME. IT PLAYS UPON MY STRONG DESIRES.

EVEN THOUGH I MUST REMAIN HERE TO SHOW OTHERS THE WAY.

OH, MY DEAR LORD...

...IF ONLY EVERYONE UNDERSTOOD YOU LIKE I DO, THEY WOULDN'T FIGHT YOU SO.

YES... IT IS WOEFUL THEY DO NOT COME TO SEEK THE GREAT WISDOM WHICH IS TREASURED IN MY BOSOM.

THESE ARE THE SORT OF THINGS I ENJOY SPEAKING OF.

THEN I CAN TELL YOU SLÁINE WILL DIE SLOWLY...

JUST AS AN INFANT WHO DOES NOT WISH TO LEAVE HIS MOTHER'S WOMB STRUGGLES AND HOWLS AS HE ENTERS THE WORLD, SO SLÁINE WILL STRUGGLE AND HOWL AS HE LEAVES IT...

HIS WILL BE... A DIFFICULT DEATH.

FOR I SHALL BE ACTING AS MIDWIFE!

"AND SO MEDB RETURNED TO MURIAS... SNIFF!... TO PLOT SLÁINE'S DOWNFALL..."

"ALTHOUGH I HAD NO IDEA SHE'D... SNIFF! ...CONSULTED WITH THE LORD WEIRD... OR HER TRUE IDENTITY... I REALISED SHE WAS UP TO NO GOOD... SNIFF!' ..."

UKKO..?

"SO I TRIED TO ALERT SLÁINE, BUT HE WAS TOO BUSY MAKING..."

OH, SOTH... IT'S NO USE. I CAN'T GO ON...

I'VE NEVER SEEN YOU LIKE THIS...

UKKO, WHAT'S WRONG?

UKKO..? PLEASE...TELL ME WHAT'S UPSETTING YOU...

LEAVE ME ALONE!

"SO I TRIED TO ALERT SLÁINE ABOUT MEDB, BUT HE WAS TOO BUSY MAKING PLANS FOR THE ARRIVAL OF KING RUDRAIGE AND HIS WIFE..."

"...WHO WERE COMING TO MURIAS TO DISCUSS A UNION BETWEEN THEIR TRIBES... FOR RUDRAIGE WAS THE HOLDER OF THE SILVER SWORD OF THE MOON..."

I WAS WRONG ABOUT YOU, UKKO. I NEVER KNEW YOU CARED ABOUT THE TERRIBLE EVENTS THAT BEFELL TIR NAN OG...

I'M RIGHT, AREN'T I? THAT IS WHAT'S UPSETTING YOU..?

NOT EXACTLY... SNIFF.'

YOU KNOW WHAT THE EVER-LIVING ONES PAY ME TO RECORD SLÁINE'S DEEDS..? EH..?

TWO IRON BARS A CHAPTER!

IT'S THE THOUGHT THAT SOME DAY SOME SKRUNK'S GOING TO MAKE MONEY OUT OF THIS SAGA... AND IT WON'T BE ME!

YOU WANT TO TRY LIVING ON TWO IRON BARS!

Iron bars were Celtic currency. Throughout Ukko's saga there are snide comments in the margins about not receiving enough for his work.
As far as his comments about future exploitation of his work are concerned, it should be pointed out. that the cost of deciphering, translating and adapting his original manuscript is considerable and his stories are being published purely for their legendary value, rather than for reasons of profit.

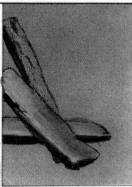

YOU'RE SO *PURSE-PROUD*, UKKO. IT'S A GREAT *HONOUR* TO BE ASKED TO WRITE A SAGA LIKE THIS...

IT'S REALLY WORTH DOING FOR *NOTHING*.

AAUUUGGHH!!

AN EVER-LIVING ONE BURST IN...

WHAT IS IT?

I THINK HE'S HAD SOME SORT OF *SEIZURE!*

MEAD... MEAD...

GET HIS TANKARD... *QUICKLY!*

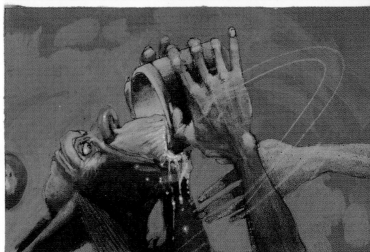

WHAT HAPPENED, UKKO?

NEVER... *NEVER* MENTION THE WORD *"NOTHING"* TO A DWARF, DEAR...

WE'RE VERY SENSITIVE TO *BAD LANGUAGE!*

AH! SLÁINE! I MUST TELL HIM ABOUT MEGRIM...

SLÁINE!

IT'S TOO NICE A DAY TO ARGUE WITH YOU, CATHBAD. HAVE YOU NOTICED HOW IT'S GETTING WARMER.

I'VE NOTICED HOW YOU IGNORE YOUR DRUID!

ONLY BECAUSE YOU IGNORE THE GODDESS...

YOU DON'T UNDERSTAND, SIRE... ALTHOUGH WE WORSHIP A FEMALE DEITY, THERE'S ALWAYS BEEN A *DARK* SIDE TO HER— THE *SAVAGERY* OF NATURE— WHICH NEEDS CONTROLLING ... GUIDING...

AND THAT'S MY JOB AS SUN KING? TO *WATCH OVER* THE EARTH MY WIFE? TO KEEP HER IN HER PLACE? PASSIVE? SUBMISSIVE?

SLÁINE... CAN I HAVE A WORD?

I PREFER... MAINTAINING THE COSMIC BALANCE, SIRE.

THE COSMIC BALANCE WILL ONLY BE ACHIEVED WHEN THE POWER OF THE GREAT GODDESS AND HER HORNED GOD IS RESTORED.

YOU SEEK TO ADVISE *ME* ON MATTERS OF RELIGION?

YES...FOR I HAVE ENTERED *THE CAULDRON OF INSPIRATION* AND TASTED *THE THREE DROPS OF WISDOM*... THE GODDESS HERSELF HAS TOLD ME THAT A *MATERNAL* SOCIETY — NOT A PATRIARCHY— IS THE NATURAL WAY OF THINGS.

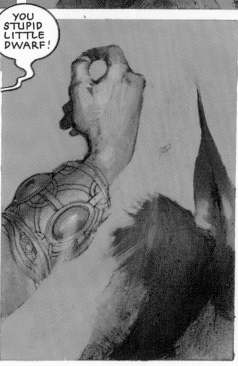

THAT NIGHT, SLÁINE'S WARRIORS GATHERED IN THE GREAT ROUND HALL, IN FRONT OF THEIR PRIVATE STALLS, AS I ANNOUNCED THE ARRIVAL OF THE ROYAL VISITORS...

KING RUDRAIGE THE MIGHTY OF THE FIR DOMAIN! THE TRIBE OF THE GROWLING SHIELDS!

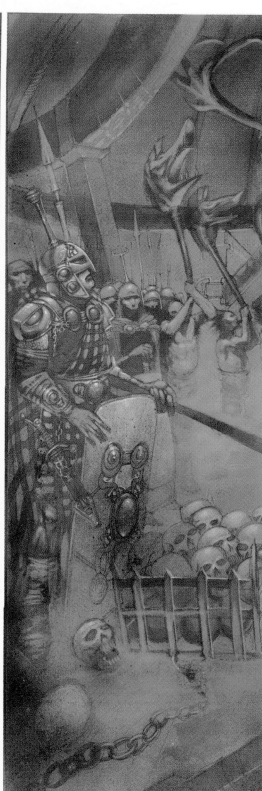

WELCOME TO MURIAS, KING RUDRAIGE.

I THANK YOU, KING SLÁINE.

ALLOW ME TO PRESENT MY WIFE...

...QUEEN NIAMH.

I UNDERSTAND YOU WANT TO FIGHT ME FOR *THE MOON SWORD* AND PERHAPS MY *BRIDE* AS WELL..?

...FOR I BELIEVE YOU WERE CLOSE TO HER ONCE...

...BUT I THINK I SHOULD WARN YOU MY WEAPON IS ENDOWED WITH *LUNAR POWER* FROM THE ANCIENT TIMES... IT DOES NOT ACTUALLY *CUT* IT'S VICTIMS...

...RATHER THEIR BODIES RIP *THEMSELVES* OPEN TO RECEIVE IT...

...AND NO DOCTOR CAN CURE SUCH A WOUND!

KRRASH!

NIAMH... I SWEAR I SEEK ONLY OUT OF LIFE WHAT *EVERYONE* SEEKS... NO MORE ...NO LESS...

WHAT IS IT THE NORSEMEN SAY..? "FODDER, FLAX, FIRE AND FRIGG."

SOMETHING TO EAT... SOMETHING TO WEAR... SOMEWHERE TO KEEP WARM...

...AND SOMEONE TO LOVE.

AND IT WOULD SEEM YOU'VE FOUND SOMEONE, TOO...

IT'S GOOD TO SEE YOU AGAIN, NIAMH.

AS MY BROTHER'S WIDOW, MEGRIM IS ENTITLED TO HER STALL IN THE ROUND HALL, BUT THAT IS ALL...

YES, AND SHE LOOKS *SO* GRIEF-STRICKEN...

WHY ARE YOU IN SUCH A BAD SKIN, NIAMH? DOESN'T MARRIAGE AGREE WITH YOU TWO?

IF IT DIDN'T, RUDRAIGE WOULDN'T HAVE TO KILL HIM-SELF TO GET AWAY FROM ME... I'VE ONLY AGREED TO AN *ANNUAL MARRIAGE.*

UNDER CELTIC LAW, IF A MAN OR WOMAN WAS UNDECIDED ABOUT THEIR PARTNER, THEY COULD AGREE TO BE BONDED FOR ONE YEAR, AT THE END OF WHICH THE MARRIAGE WAS ANNULLED OR RENEWED.

AFTER MY PAST EXPERIENCES WITH MEN, I WAS RELUCTANT TO COMMIT MYSELF TO LONGER...

FROM NOW ON, I REDDEN MY FINGERNAILS FOR MYSELF.

HOW IS OUR SON?

MY SON. YOU WERE NOT PRESENT TO SUFFER THE LABOUR PAINS WITH ME ...REMEMBER?

(IT WAS THE CUSTOM FOR MEN TO EXPERIENCE BIRTH PANGS AS WELL — BY A "GLAMOUR" BEING PUT ON THEM.)

NO ONE WAS.

AS A PUNISHMENT FOR NIAMH TAKING A LOVER, THE KING MADE HER HAVE HER CHILD ENTIRELY ON HER OWN...

I'M SORRY.

BUT KAI IS WELL. THEY SEND WORD FROM THE SEMINARY THAT HE ALREADY SHOWS A TALENT FOR POETRY...

WELL, HE CERTAINLY DOESN'T GET THAT FROM HIS FATHER!

AH, BUT HIS MOTHER IS A WOMAN OF MANY TALENTS. SHE HAS A GENIUS FOR *INVENTING* THINGS... DO YOU KNOW SHE'S DESIGNED SOME NEW BELLOWS SPEARS FOR THE TRIBE?

THE GODDESS IS REALLY IN HER...

IT'S LATE. IF WE'RE TO MAKE BATTLE PLANS TOMORROW, WE'D BETTER GET TO BED. GOOD NIGHT, SLÁINE.

AYE! GOOD NIGHT.

GOOD NIGHT...

GOOD NIGHT, BOTH. SWEET DREAMS...

SOON AFTER, THE OTHERS RETIRED, BUT SLÁINE SAT DRINKING ALONE (APART FROM HIS FAITHFUL DWARF, OF COURSE)...

AH, THE FIRST LOVE! THAT'S ALWAYS THE ONE YOU NEVER REALLY GET OVER. THERE'S ALWAYS A CORNER OF YOUR HEART PRESERVED FOR HER. I REMEMBER MINE...

...IT WAS AFTER MY MOTHER'S SECOND ATTEMPT ON MY LIFE... I'D TAKEN REFUGE ON A NEARBY FARM...

In the original manuscript there now follows a boastful and somewhat unbelievable account of Ukko's early romantic escapades. This has been deleted as being irrelevant, somewhat offensive and possibly illegal.

...I TELL YOU, AFTER THAT, I THINK I *PREFERRED* MOTHER CHAINING ME UP IN THE YARD AND BEATING ME WITH A BROOMSTICK!

GOOD NIGHT, DWARF.

SLÁINE STILL HAS EYES FOR NIAMH... ONLY WHEN SHE IS DEAD, WILL HE FINALLY BE IN MY POWER...

...AND, WITHIN THE CAULDRON, IS ONE ONLY TOO WILLING TO MAKE HER END A PARTICULARLY FOUL ONE!

AVAGDDU... THE SON OF THE EARTH GODDESS... THE UGLIEST, MOST STUPID AND FOUL CREATURE THAT EVER EXISTED. THE **DARK SIDE** OF EARTH POWER...

GREETINGS, DECAYING ONE...

YOU SMELL NICE... OF PRIMROSES... MEADOW-SWEET... AND OAK BLOSSOM.

AND YOU SMELL... BEYOND BELIEF!

THERE, THERE, DON'T VOMIT. I DO NOT MIND YOUR RANCID ODOURS... FOR I KNOW IT IS YOUR "MYSTIC AURA"... THE **SWEET PUTRESCENCE** THAT HERALDS THE ONSET OF OBLIVION.

DEATH AND DECAY... YERRR... THAT'S ME!

AND IT'S SO **SAD** HUMANS FEAR AND FIGHT YOU WHEN YOU'RE ONLY TRYING TO **HELP** THEM REACH THE HIGHER PLANES OF EXISTENCE BY SPREADING YOUR HIDEOUS GIFTS AMONGST THEM.

MOTHER SAYS I'M DISGUSTING... AND PUTRID... AND STOOOOPID!

AND YOU **ARE**, DECAYING ONE! YOU ARE! BUT THE LORD WEIRD TAUGHT ME AS A CHILD I SHOULD **WELCOME** DEATH AND DECAY.

THEY FORGET **SICKNESS**... **WASTE**... AND **CORRUPTION** ARE NATURAL... A VITAL PART OF THE CYCLE OF NATURE... THAT THEY **MUST** RETURN TO THE EARTH FOR **NEW LIFE** TO GROW OUT OF **THEM**...

BUT I NEVER GET **ENOUGH** HUMANS TO FEED ON! I'M ALWAYS HUNGRY FOR **MORE**!

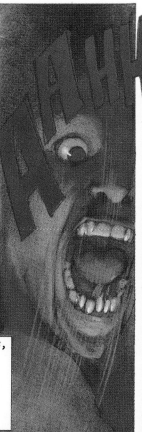

AAHHHHH!

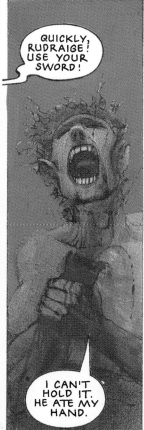

QUICKLY, RUDRAIGE! USE YOUR SWORD!

I CAN'T HOLD IT. HE ATE MY HAND.

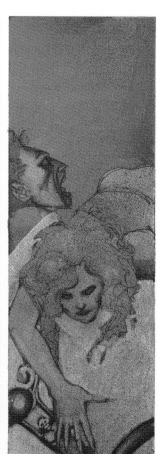

UNFORTUNATELY FOR MEDB, THERE'S STUPID, THERE'S STUPIDER, AND THERE'S AVAGDDU. AS THICK AS THE LIFTING BAR OF A CAULDRON, HE BEGAN EATING RUDRAIGE'S HAND, BELIEVING IT WAS NIAMH'S.

ALTHOUGH THE SWORD COULD KILL ANY LIVING CREATURE, IT HAD NO EFFECT ON A DEMON FROM THE OTHERWORLD.

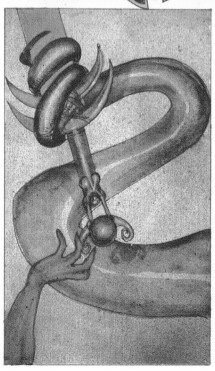

GET OFF OF ME!

NIAMH!

AS THICK AS A CASTLE WALL...

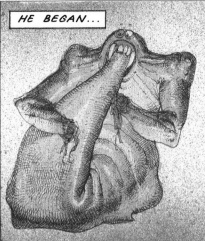

HE BEGAN...

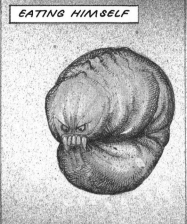

EATING HIMSELF

UNTIL

THERE WAS NOTHING

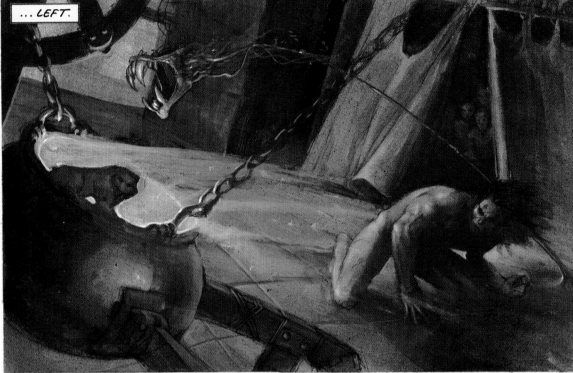

...LEFT.

WHAT HAPPENED? WHAT'S BEEN GOING ON..?

HE SUMMONED A...CREATURE FROM HIS CAULDRON TO KILL RUDRAIGE!

I THOUGHT YOU'D CHANGED, SLÁINE, BUT YOU'VE JUST BECOME SLYER ...YOU WERE MAD WITH JEALOUSY, SO YOU THOUGHT YOU'D GET RID OF YOUR RIVAL, THEN DO YOUR BIG MALE "HERO" ACT AND RESCUE ME!

BOOK 2

BY NOT TREATING NIAMH AS A PIECE OF PROPERTY TO BE FOUGHT AND WON ...BY SEEKING PEACE WITH HER HUSBAND, RATHER THAN WAR, SLÁINE HAD SHOWN HE REALLY WAS *TRYING* TO FOLLOW THE WAY OF THE HORNED GOD...

...UNFORTUNATELY, NIAMH DIDN'T BELIEVE A WORD OF IT. DESPITE HIS PROTESTS, SHE WAS CONVINCED HE WAS RESPONSIBLE FOR AVAGDDU ATTACKING RUDRAIGE...

I FOUND HER THE NEXT DAY FASHIONING *A SILVER CLAW* TO REPLACE RUDRAIGE'S HAND...

LISTEN, DEAR, SLÁINE DIDN'T SUMMON THAT DEMON. HE REALLY *HAS* CHANGED.

EVER SINCE HE ENTERED THE VERY CAULDRON AVAGDDU CAME OUT OF, I SUPPOSE?

THAT'S RIGHT...IT'S THE CAULDRON OF INSPIRATION, AS WELL, YOU SEE.

AND I SUPPOSE HE ASKED YOU TO SPEAK ON HIS BEHALF?

NO. THAT WAS MY IDEA. YOU SEE, WHENEVER SLÁINE'S IN A BAD MOOD, HE ALWAYS TAKES IT OUT ON ME!

YOU'RE PROBABLY TELLING THE TRUTH. FOR ONCE. I CAN'T THINK OF A MORE UNLIKELY PERSON TO PLEAD HIS CASE.

MEANWHILE...SLÁINE WAS DEMONSTRATING TO RUDRAIGE'S WARRIORS HOW THE SESSAIR USED THE GAE BOLGA...

ONE WAY IS TO DROP TO THE GROUND...PRETENDING YOU'RE WOUNDED...

SO YOUR ENEMY LOWERS HIS SHIELD AND CLOSES IN FOR THE KILL...

THEN PICK UP AND THROW THE SPEAR WITH YOUR FOOT...

...BECAUSE WHEN YOU'RE LYING DOWN, YOUR BUTTOCK AND THIGH MUSCLES ARE THE MOST POWERFUL IN YOUR BODY.

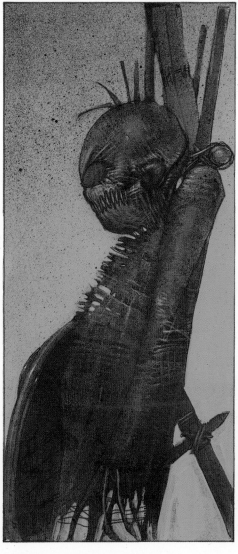

DUFF!

THEN MOVE IN...

AND...

...*RIP* IT OUT TEARING OUT HIS INSIDES!

ER... SLÁINE... YOU KNOW I WANTED A WORD WITH YOU THE OTHER DAY?

WHAT OF IT, DWARF?

IT'S ABOUT MEGRIM... I THINK SHE'S WORKING FOR THE DRUNE LORDS!

YOU'RE ACCUSING HER OF *TREASON?*

YES... YOU SEE THE OTHER NIGHT I WATCHED HER PREPARING STRANGE POTIONS IN THE FOREST, AND...

UKKO, IT IS AGAINST THE LAW TO DISCUSS POLITICS IN *PRIVATE.*

NO, WAIT, LISTEN! SHE REMINDS ME OF THAT GIRL WE MET IN THE SOUTH CALLED *MEDB*... THE BRIDE OF CROM! REMEMBER HER?

UKKO, THE *REASON* IT'S AGAINST THE LAW IS TO PREVENT PEOPLE LIKE YOU STIRRING UP TROUBLE!

ANY ACCUSATION YOU WISH TO MAKE ABOUT MEGRIM MUST BE MADE IN PUBLIC— BEFORE THE GENERAL ASSEMBLY... WHERE SHE IS FREE TO ANSWER IT.

AND IF THE CHARGE PROVES FALSE, YOU WILL BE SENTENCED TO DEATH BY SUFFOCATION IN THE NEAREST BOG.

OH, WELL... FORGET IT THEN!

BUT DON'T SAY I DIDN'T WARN YOU ABOUT HER!

SIRE, I THINK YOU SHOULD HAVE A LOOK AT *THE KNUCKER*.

HE'S NOT HIS OLD VICIOUS SELF. HE'S ONLY EATEN ONE GOAT IN THE LAST THREE DAYS.

IT'S THIS *WARM* WEATHER THAT'S MAKING HIM SLUGGISH. IF IT CONTINUES, HE COULD EVEN GO INTO *HIBERNATION*.

THE KNUCKER WAS DESCENDED FROM *THE ICE DRAGONS* OF OLD... *COLD* GAVE THEM *ENERGY* AND SUITED THEIR UNIQUE METHOD OF FLIGHT: GLIDING ON THE HOT AIR THERMALS PRODUCED BY THEIR FIERY BREATH.

I NEED HIM TO FLY TO *FINIAS*, MONGAN.

YOU'VE STILL HAD NO REPLY TO YOUR OFFER OF AN ALLIANCE?

NO. I FEAR KING GANN HASN'T FORGOTTEN THE DAYS WHEN WE USED TO STEAL HIS CATTLE.

AYE. WE CELTS BEAR GRUDGES A LONG TIME.

BUT WITHOUT HIS *SPEAR OF THE SUN* WE CANNOT BE SURE OF VICTORY.

SO YOU *STILL* SEEK *THE FORBIDDEN WEAPONS?*

I WARNED YOU OF THE DANGERS, BUT YOU WOULDN'T LISTEN, WOULD YOU? AND NOW WE MUST *ALL* PAY FOR YOUR PIG-HEADEDNESS.

WHAT ARE YOU TALKING ABOUT, CATHBAD?

POWER IS SURGING FROM THE STONES AT CARNAC ...MELTING THE ICE... *THE SUDDEN THAW* WILL CAUSE *A DELUGE*, DROWNING THE EARTH!

IF YOU'RE RIGHT, SURELY THAT IS THE WORK OF SLOUGH FEG..? HARDLY THE GODDESS.

SHE IS *USING* FEG TO MAKE US RETURN TO HER WATERY WOMB. A *SIREN* LURING US TO OUR DOOM!

NOW DO YOU SEE WHY NATURE NEEDS *CONTROLLING?* AND WHY YOU *MUST* STOP YOUR INSANE QUEST FOR HER TREASURES?

CONVINCED THE GODDESS
WOULD NEVER BETRAY
HIM, SLÁINE IGNORED
CATHBAD'S WARNINGS...

TRAVELLING BY NIGHT
WHEN THE AIR WAS
COOLER AND THE
KNUCKER MORE
ENERGETIC, WE
REACHED THE CITY OF
FINIAS LATE THE
FOLLOWING EVENING...

INSIDE, *KING GANN* MADE US WELCOME...
HE WAS A DOUR WIDOWER WITH A
RATHER CYNICAL OUTLOOK ON LIFE, WHO
SLAINE TOOK AN INSTANT LIKING TO...

WITH THE SEA DEMONS PLUNDERING YOUR LAND? STEALING YOUR CATTLE?

I THOUGHT ABOUT REPLYING TO YOUR CALL FOR A TRIBAL CONFEDERATION, BUT TO BE HONEST, I COULDN'T SEE THE POINT. WE'RE ALL RIGHT AS WE ARE.

WELL... THEY WON'T BE THE FIRST, WILL THEY?

OCH, WE USED TO DO THE SAME TO YOU... IT'S ALL WATER UNDER THE BRIDGE NOW... WE'VE LEARNT TO LIVE ON *BARKS* AND *ROOTS* INSTEAD.

BUT IF YOU JOIN US, YOU CAN SHARE IN THE CAULDRON THAT FEEDS ALL WHO COME BEFORE IT— WITH GREAT PIECES OF *BEEF* AND *PORK* AND *LAMB*.

MORE THAN YOU CAN DIG YOUR FLESH FORK IN!

WE'RE QUITE HAPPY WITH *TURNIPS*.

AREN'T WE?

OH, AYE.

AYE.

AYE.

RECOGNISING GANN, THE SPEAR BEGAN STRAINING AGAINST ITS THONGS AND HOWLING AND MOANING ... EAGER TO KILL...

I'LL HAVE TO GIVE IT ITS SLEEPING DRAUGHT OF POPPY LEAVES SOON, OR IT'LL BE UNCONTROLLABLE.

IT HAS THE FACE OF A WOMAN, YET YOU CALL IT THE SPEAR OF LUG THE SUN GOD?

WELL, IT DATES BACK TO THE ANCIENT TIMES WHEN THE SUN WAS WORSHIPPED AS A GODDESS AND THERE WERE NO GODS. BUT YOU KNOW WHAT OUR PRIESTS ARE LIKE...

ONLY TOO WELL. THEY FEAR THE MOTHER OF ALL AND SEEK TO MAKE US CONTROL HER.

OCH, WHEN YOU LOOK AT THAT SPEAR, CAN YOU BLAME THEM? SHE'S A BLOODTHIRSTY BITCH.

AYE!

AYE!

AYE!

ER—DOES ANYONE MIND IF I STICK TO MEAD?

NOW...YOU MIGHT THINK SLÁINE WAS *MAD*...BUT YOU HAVE TO UNDERSTAND THAT *CELTS GAIN STATUS* BY GIVING THINGS AWAY...

THE *BIGGER* THE *GIFT*— THE *GREATER* THE STATUS...

NOW IMAGINE WHAT A *STATUS SYMBOL* IT WAS FOR SLÁINE... GIVING HIS *WHOLE TRIBE* AWAY!

YES...IF YOU ASK ME, SLÁINE DID IT JUST SO HE COULD LOOK *BIG!*

THAT'S A *HORRIBLE* THING TO WRITE, UKKO!

WELL, IT'S *TRUE!* I REMEMBER WHEN HE USED TO SAY TO ME... "I'LL DO THINGS THEY'LL TALK ABOUT FOREVER."

HE WAS *ALWAYS* SHOWING OFF!

YOU'VE GOT IT ALL WRONG, UKKO... SLÁINE OFFERED HIS TRIBE TO KING GANN TO SHOW HE WAS FOLLOWING THE WAY OF THE HORNED GOD ...*SHARING POWER* WITH OTHER MEN.

SO..? AM I MEANT TO BE IMPRESSED..?

WELL, YES... IF YOU LOOK AT MOST SO-CALLED "HEROES", YOU'LL SEE THEY'RE USUALLY SOLITARY, MOODY MEN WHO LIKE TO DO IT ON THEIR OWN.

EH?

I MEAN, THEY'RE NOT USED TO *COOPERATING* LIKE *WOMEN*. SO IT WAS A *BIG STEP* FORWARD FOR SLÁINE.

AND I STILL SAY HE DID IT FOR *THE PRESTIGE. THAT'S* THE *REAL* REASON YOU CELTS ARE SO GENEROUS, YOU KNOW... SO YOU CAN *SHOW OFF* ABOUT IT AFTERWARDS!

"OH, LOOK WHAT *I* GAVE AWAY! AREN'T *I* WONDERFUL? AREN'T *I* KIND AND GENEROUS?"

YOU'RE SUCH A NASTY PIECE OF WORK. THIS IS MEANT TO BE A ROMANTIC, *BEAUTIFUL* SAGA AND YOU KEEP MAKING ALL THESE *SNIDE HORRIBLE* COMMENTS...

...*WHY* DO YOU HAVE TO *SPOIL* EVERYTHING?

NOT ME, DEAR... OH, NO!

IT WAS *MEDB* WHO DID THE SPOILING!

YOU SEE, KNOWING SLÁINE WAS TRYING TO ARRANGE AN ALLIANCE WITH KING GANN, SHE SUMMONED A **GHOSTLY DRAGON** FROM THE OTHER-WORLD TO PREVENT IT...

"NO, NO, UKKO... DON'T SAY 'SUMMONED'... SAY 'INVITED'...

"BECAUSE A MERE HUMAN CANNOT 'SUMMON' A **PAN-DIMENSIONAL** BEING INTO OUR WORLD... YOU 'INVITE' THEM...

"AND IF THEY FIND THE IDEA AMUSING... THEY MAY AGREE TO DO YOUR BIDDING...

"AND DON'T CALL IT A DRAGON-*GHOST*, EITHER..."

"YOU SEE, THE WORLD THIS CREATURE IS FROM IS FAR MORE 'REAL' THAN OUR OWN... WE'RE LIKE DRAWINGS OF PEOPLE ON A CAVE WALL TO IT..."

"TO THE DRAGONS... *HUMANS* ARE THE GHOSTS..."

"LOOK, DEAR, AM I WRITING THIS SAGA OR ARE YOU?"

"YOU ARE, OF COURSE, UKKO... I WOULDN'T DREAM OF INTERFERING..."

"AFTER ALL, *YOU* WERE THERE AT THE TIME..."

"OH, *THANK YOU!* I'M GLAD YOU REMEMBERED THAT."

WHAT'S GOING ON OUTSIDE?

"AS I WAS SAYING... MEDB *SUMMONED* A *GHOSTLY DRAGON* TO ATTACK GANN'S FORTRESS, SO EVERYONE WOULD THINK..."

SIRE! SIRE! SLÁINE'S DRAGON'S ESCAPED!

IT'S BURNING DOWN THE CITY!

TREACHERY!

THIS "ALLIANCE" WAS A TRICK TO ALLAY MY SUSPICIONS! I SHOULD HAVE KNOWN THE SESSAIR WOULD NEVER CHANGE!

BITTER YOUR WORDS, GANN — BUT THEY'RE NOT TRUE, I SWEAR IT.

OUTSIDE, THE WOODED BATTLEMENTS TOPPING THE STONE RAMPARTS WERE ABLAZE...

SENSING THE PRESENCE OF A RIVAL, THE KNUCKER WAS BELLOWING AND HOWLING TO BE FREED...

THE KNUCKER'S JEWELLED EYES SCANNED THE NIGHT SKY FOR THE DRAGON-GHOST... BUT THE ELEMENTAL HAD VANISHED...

THEY'RE OUT OF RANGE OF OUR WEAPONS, SIRE.

BUT NOT *THE SPEAR OF LUG!*

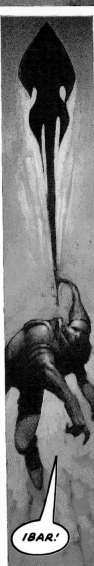

IBAR!

SAVOURING THE PROSPECT OF AN EASY KILL, THE PHANTOM DRAGON COULD NOT RESIST ATTACKING THE DYING KNUCKER...

FOR A FEW MOMENTS, SLÁINE'S SERPENT REGAINED SOMETHING OF ITS OLD SAVAGERY...

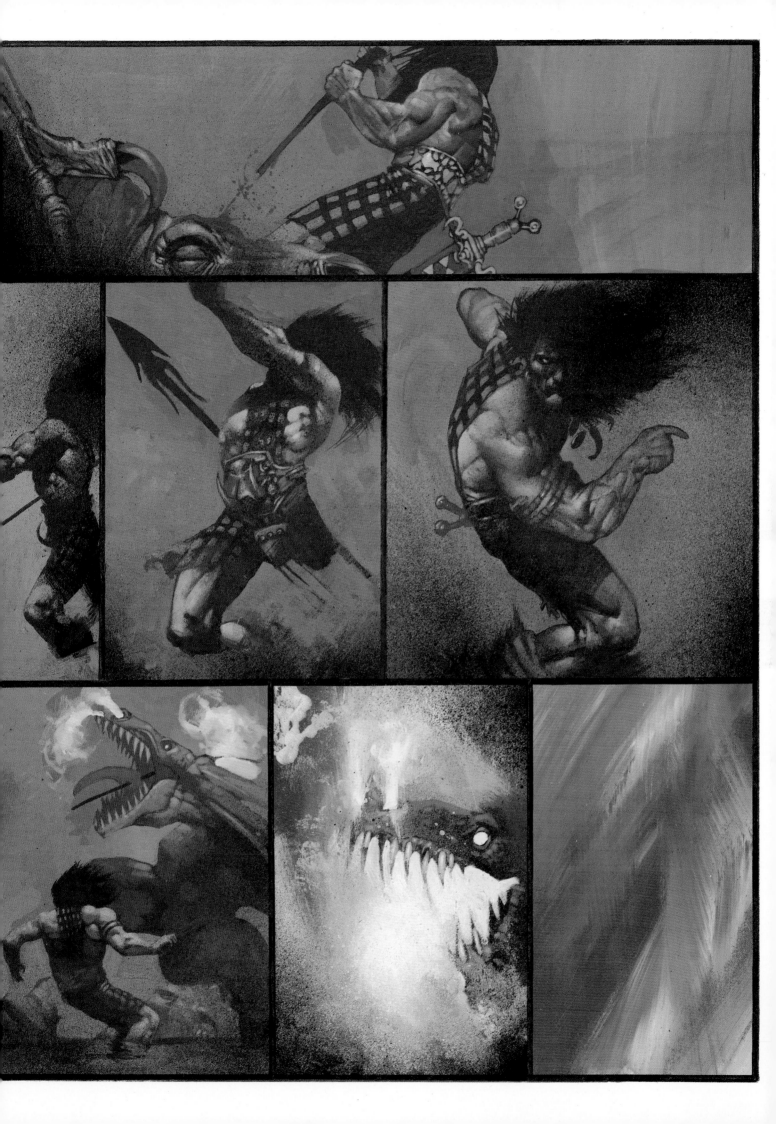

KING GANN PROVIDED SLÁINE AND I WITH SUITABLE MOUNTS AND WE RETURNED TO MURIAS... ALTHOUGH SLÁINE NOW BELIEVED MEGRIM WAS RESPONSIBLE FOR THE SUPERNATURAL ATTACKS, HE IGNORED MY ADVICE (TO EXECUTE HER IMMEDIATELY)... TELLING ME HE WANTED TO WAIT UNTIL HE KNEW FOR CERTAIN WHO SHE REALLY WAS...

NOW ALL THAT REMAINED WAS FOR HIM TO OBTAIN *THE LAST* OF THE TREASURES... *THE LIA FAIL, THE SACRED STONE OF DESTINY... THE NAVEL OF THE GODDESS...*

IT WAS HELD IN THE GREAT *ISLAND CITY OF FALIAS...* CAPITAL OF *THE TRIBE OF THE SHADOWS...*

SO CALLED BECAUSE THEY PAINTED THEIR BODIES AND SHIELDS **BLACK** AND PREFERRED TO FIGHT ON REALLY DARK NIGHTS...

UNFORTUNATELY... SOMEONE ELSE ALREADY SOUGHT THE STONE...

THEY CALLED HIM *THE AVANC.*

HE WAS THE LAST OF **THE BEAVER FOLK** WHO BUILT THEIR HOMES WITH SUBMERGED ENTRANCES IN THE MARSHES ON THE EDGE OF THE GREAT INLAND SEA... AND WHICH GAVE THEM THEIR NAME.

THEY WERE A DIFFERENT, WISER RACE OF HUMANS ... GENTLE PEACE-LOVING **MOON-WORSHIPPERS** ...SLEEPING BY DAY, ONLY COMING ALIVE DURING THE HOURS OF DARKNESS.

THEY WERE **HAPPY.**

AND THEN **THE SUN HEROES** CAME.

AND THEY LOOKED AT THE BEAVER FOLK WITH BONE-RIDGED "HORNS" OVER THEIR EYES... LURKING IN THE DEPTHS OF THE BOGS... AND THEY CALLED THEM...

"DEVILS".

AND BEGAN EXTERMINATING THEM AS SUN HEROES USUALLY DO — IN THE NAME OF "PROGRESS" AND "CIVILISATION".

AND BUILT A GREAT CITY OVER THE REMAINS OF THEIR LODGES... **FALIAS,** CITY OF SCREAMING SHADOWS...

CITY OF THE DAMNED.

HE HAD NEVER ENTERED THE CITY BEFORE... HE HAD BEEN TOO AFRAID OF THE SUN HEROES.

BUT HE SENSED INSTINCTIVELY THE WAY... UP THROUGH THE FOUNDATIONS OF THE CITY... THROUGH THE TUNNELS OF HIS ANCESTORS.

THROUGH THE LODGES WHERE THEY'D HUDDLED TOGETHER AND MADE THEIR LAST STAND... FIGHTING WITH BARE FANGS AGAINST WEAPONS OF IRON AND BRONZE.

THE FEW WHO ESCAPED HAD FOUND REFUGE ELSEWHERE... IN A CAVE AT THE BOTTOM OF THE SEA... WHERE THEY WERE SAFE— EVEN FROM SUN HEROES.

THEN, ONE BY ONE, THEY, TOO, WENT ON...

RETURNING TO THE MOON MOTHER.

AND THERE WAS JUST THE AVANC LEFT.

ALTHOUGH HE WAS NOT ALONE. FOR THE VOICES OF HIS ANCESTORS WERE WITH HIM ALWAYS... LAUGHING AND COMFORTING HIM...

PREPARING HIM FOR THE MOMENT WHEN HE, TOO, MUST GO ON.

HE HAD NEVER ENTERED THE CITY BEFORE... HE HAD BEEN TOO AFRAID OF THE SUN HEROES.

UNTIL NOW.

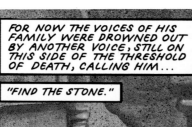

FOR NOW THE VOICES OF HIS FAMILY WERE DROWNED OUT BY ANOTHER VOICE, STILL ON THIS SIDE OF THE THRESHOLD OF DEATH, CALLING HIM...

"FIND THE STONE."

ORDERING HIM...

"FIND THE STONE."

HOUNDING HIM, EVEN IN HIS DREAMS, UNTIL HE DID ITS BIDDING...

"FIND THE STONE, YOU APE... FIND THE STONE!"

IN THE GREAT HALL, KING SENGANN, TOO, HEARD VOICES IN HIS HEAD, AS HE DRANK ALONE... COUNTING THE HOURS UNTIL DAWN...

HOW MUCH LONGER?

ANOTHER THREE HOURS, ACCORDING TO THE WATER CLOCK, SIRE.

THREE HOURS TILL HE COULD CLOSE HIS EYES AND BLOT OUT THE SHADOWS CAST BY THE FIRELIGHT...

...OF THE SCREAMING MEN, WOMEN AND CHILDREN OF THE BEAVER FOLK.

OF HIS WARRIORS CUTTING THEM DOWN.

MUTILATING THEM BEFORE THEY DIED...

THREE HOURS UNTIL THE SCREAMING STOPPED!

ALTHOUGH, LIKE THE REST OF HIS TRIBE, KING SENGANN PAINTED HIMSELF BLACK, THE DARK RINGS ROUND HIS EYES WERE NOT TATTOOS... BUT TINTED BY LONG NIGHTS OF TERROR...

EVER SINCE THEY'D STOLEN THE STONE.

THEY'D TAKEN THE BEAVER FOLK'S SACRED TREASURE AS A TROPHY... A SYMBOL OF THEIR GREAT VICTORY OVER THE "DEVILS".

AND, UNDER ITS BALEFUL INFLUENCE, HIS TRIBE HAD SLOWLY TURNED FROM SUN HEROES INTO MOON WORSHIPPERS... SLEEPING BY DAY, ONLY COMING ALIVE DURING THE HOURS OF DARKNESS.

LIKE THE PEOPLE THEY'D SLAIN.

WHO SPOKE TO HIM EVERY NIGHT... IF **ONLY** THEY WOULD **STOP**... IF ONLY THERE COULD BE AN **END** TO IT ALL...

"KILL!" THE VOICE COMMANDED HIM.

"NOW...THE STONE."

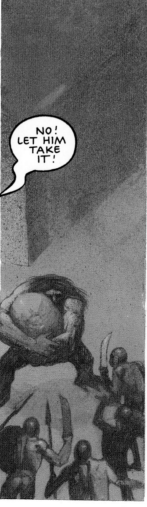

NO! LET HIM TAKE IT!

MAYBE THEN THE CURSE ON US WILL BE LIFTED...

MAYBE THEN I'LL BE FREE...

THE AVANC HAS TAKEN THE STONE TO THE LAIR AT THE BOTTOM OF THE SEA...WHERE NONE DARE VENTURE, EVEN IF THEY COULD HOLD THEIR BREATH LONG ENOUGH TO FIND IT.

ONCE AGAIN OUR PLANS ARE FRUSTRATED. THIS IS TOO MUCH OF A COINCIDENCE.

AYE!

NO DOUBT THE LORD WEIRD HAS MANAGED TO CONTROL THIS APE CREATURE BY *SORCERY*, SIRE.

NO DOUBT.

SO, HOW WILL YOU RECOVER IT FROM THE SEA BED, SLÁINE? WHAT CUNNING PLAN HAVE YOU GOT UP YOUR SLEEVE?

SIRE..? WHAT ARE YOU GOING TO DO?

I DON'T KNOW.

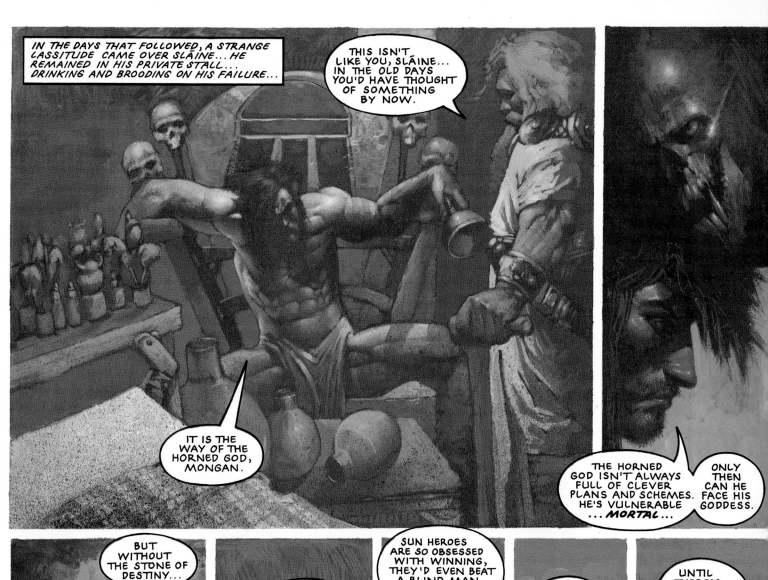

IN THE DAYS THAT FOLLOWED, A STRANGE LASSITUDE CAME OVER SLÁINE... HE REMAINED IN HIS PRIVATE STALL... DRINKING AND BROODING ON HIS FAILURE...

THIS ISN'T LIKE YOU, SLÁINE... IN THE OLD DAYS YOU'D HAVE THOUGHT OF SOMETHING BY NOW.

IT IS THE WAY OF THE HORNED GOD, MONGAN.

THE HORNED GOD ISN'T ALWAYS FULL OF CLEVER PLANS AND SCHEMES. HE'S VULNERABLE ...MORTAL...

ONLY THEN CAN HE FACE HIS GODDESS.

BUT WITHOUT THE STONE OF DESTINY...

I KNOW. WE LOSE EVERYTHING.

BUT DON'T YOU SEE, THERE'S NO SHAME IN LOSING. IT'S ONLY SUN HEROES WHO'VE TAUGHT US THERE IS.

SUN HEROES ARE SO OBSESSED WITH WINNING, THEY'D EVEN BEAT A BLIND MAN AT "WOODEN WISDOM"...

BECAUSE THEY'RE AFRAID OF FAILURE...OF DEATH...

THEY HAVE TO CONQUER EVERYTHING IN THEIR PATH... RIDING ON...

UNTIL THERE'S NOTHING LEFT TO DESTROY...

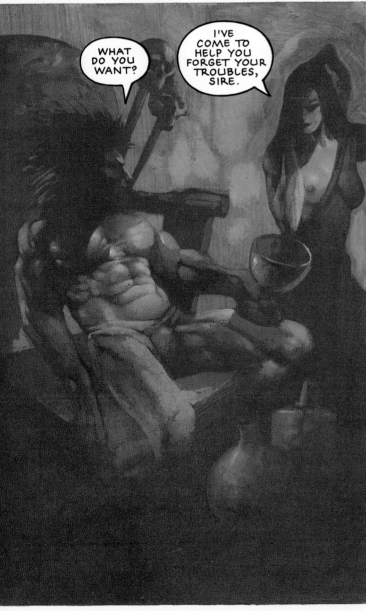

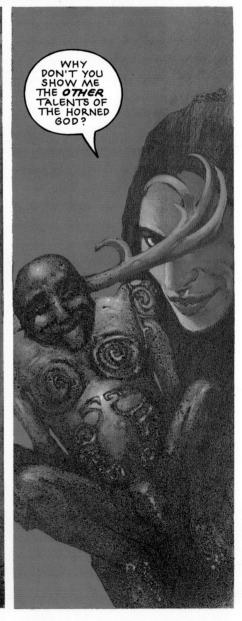

IN HIS WOMB-LIKE CAVE BENEATH THE SEA, **THE AVANC** CRADLED **THE NAVEL OF THE GODDESS**... ROCKING TO AND FRO, CROONING TO IT...

THE HARSH VOICE INSIDE HIS HEAD WAS GONE NOW AND HE FELT AT PEACE.

FOR THE ANCIENT TREASURE OF HIS PEOPLE WAS RETURNED TO THEM AT LAST.

AND IT SEEMED TO THIS LONELY CREATURE THAT THE STONE WAS SINGING TO **HIM** ... ROCKING **HIM** TO SLEEP...

AND AT LAST HE SLEPT... MEETING HIS DEAD WIFE AND FRIENDS AGAIN IN HIS DREAMS... CURLED UP IN THE FOETAL POSITION IN THE BELLY OF THE GODDESS.

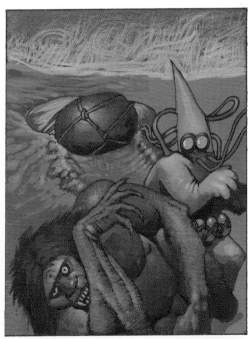

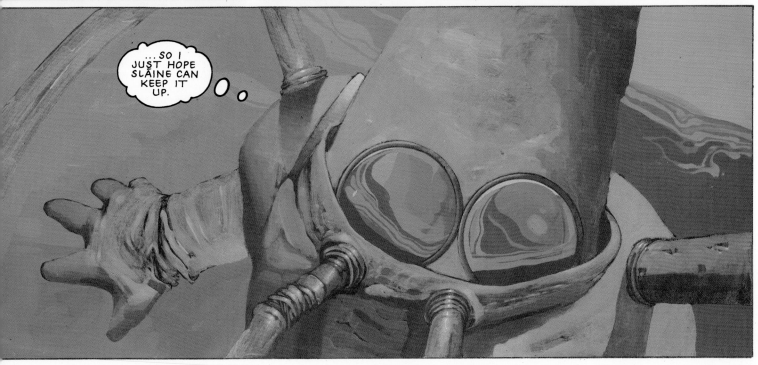

"WHAT ARE YOU WAITING FOR, YOU STUPID BEAST? DO IT!"

BUT HE COULDN'T... ALTHOUGH THIS SMOOTH SKIN WAS NOT BEAUTIFUL LIKE HIS MATE, YET HE SENSED HER FEMALENESS...

SHE WAS THE INSTRUMENT OF THE GODDESS...

OO-K!

SHE HAD SEVERED THE UMBILICAL CORD CONNECTING HIM WITH LIFE.

AND NOW HE WAS BEING CALLED HOME... TO REJOIN HIS LOVED ONES.

"KILL HER!"

MWWWUURH!!

BUT IT WAS HIS TIME... NOT HERS...

...TO GO ON.

ARRIVING BACK AT MURIAS, WE LEARNT FROM SLÁINE THAT MEGRIM WAS IN FACT THE WITCH MEDB... AND HOW, IMMEDIATELY AFTER SUMMONING THE AVANC, SHE HAD VANISHED...

WITH MEDB SAFELY OUT OF THE WAY, THE INAUGURATION CEREMONY WENT AHEAD WITHOUT INCIDENT: THE FOUR KINGS GATHERED ON THE SACRED HILL KNOWN AS *BOLG DANU...THE BELLY OF THE GODDESS...*

IN THE DISTANCE, TWO MORE SACRED HILLS COMPLETED THE OUTLINE OF THE DEITY...

THE *STONE OF DESTINY* WAS PLACED IN A SMALL HOLE IN THE SUMMIT TO FORM *THE OMPHALOS... HER NAVEL...*

THEN EACH KING, TAKING THE TWO REMAINING TREASURES, *THE SWORD OF THE MOON* AND *THE SPEAR OF THE SUN* (SPECIALLY DRUGGED FOR THE OCCASION), APPROACHED THE STONE...

AND *THE CAULDRON OF BLOOD* POSITIONED IN FRONT OF IT...

FIRST *KING GANN...*

NOTHING... AH, WELL, I DIDN'T THINK IT WOULD BE ME...I'M NOT BOTHERED, ANYWAY...

NEXT, **KING SENGANN**, WHO HAD TO BE DRAGGED SCREAMING TO THE STONE...

...BUT WHO RECEIVED NO ANSWERING CRY FROM THE LIA FAIL.

THEN... **KING RUDRAIGE**...

BUT NO ONE WHO HAD A PERSONAL BLEMISH COULD BECOME HIGH KING...

SNIFF! SULK

AND FINALLY...

KING SLÃINE.

IT CRIES OUT ITS APPROVAL! TRULY HE IS THE ARD RI... *THE KING OF KINGS!*

AND FROM THE CAULDRON...HOLDING A GLEAMING SILVER HELMET...

...THE GODDESS AS **BLODEUWEDD**... THE LADY OF THE FLOWERS...

CLOSE YOUR EYES, UKKO! IT IS NOT PERMITTED FOR THE VULGAR TO LOOK ON HER BEAUTY!

NO. LEAVE THEM OPEN, UKKO. FOR I AM NOT ASHAMED OF MY BODY THE EARTH.

NNEHHH!

NEST..?

YES, UKKO?

HOW ABOUT A *BREAK?* I'VE GOT ALL THE *GREAT BATTLES* TO WRITE ABOUT NEXT... *AND SLÁINE'S WARP-OUT*... AND *MEDB'S REVENGE*... IT'S *EXHAUSTING STUFF!*

I SHOULD HAVE THOUGHT YOU'D *ENJOY* ALL THAT *VIOLENCE.*

I WILL! BUT I PROMISED *MOR RONNE,* THE DUNG COLLECTOR, I'D HAVE A FEW DRINKS WITH HIM AFTER HE FINISHED EMPTYING *THE FORTRESS CESSPITS.*

IT'S OUT OF THE QUESTION...

...YOU MUST PRAY TO *OGMIOS,* THE GREAT GOD OF LITERATURE, INVENTOR OF THE SACRED OGHAM ALPHABET, FOR *INSPIRATION* AND GUIDANCE.

NEHHHHHH!

O, *OGMIOS*... GREAT GOD OF LITERATURE... SUPREME HACK... LOOK WITH FAVOUR ON THY HUMBLE SERVANT, UKKO THE DWARF, I BESEECH YOU.

PSST! HOW ABOUT KNOCKING OUT A COUPLE OF QUICK CHAPTERS FOR ME? EH, OGGEY? AS A FAVOUR FROM ONE HACK TO ANOTHER?

THE TRIBES OF THE EARTH GODDESS RODE OUT TO CONFRONT THEM...

...LED BY THEIR HIGH KING—SLÁINE...

THE NEW HORNED GOD.

THEY GATHERED BY THE FROZEN WATERS OF THE INNER SEA FOR "THE MUSTER"...

...UNDER THIS ANCIENT LAW, THE LAST TO ARRIVE FOR A BATTLE WAS EXECUTED IN HONOUR OF THE GODDESS.

IT ALSO ENCOURAGED PUNCTUALITY.

BOOK 3

FROM THEIR GREAT CITIES THEY CAME... *THE TRIBES OF THE EARTH GODDESS DANU*... COMMANDED BY THEIR FIVE MIGHTY KINGS...

KING GANN OF MURIAS... HIS BROTHER KING GENANN OF FINIAS... THE BOY-KING RUDRAIGE OF GORIAS... MAD KING SENGANN OF FALIAS...

AND THE ARD RI... *THE KING OF KINGS... SLÁINE.*

...TO DO BATTLE WITH **THE FOMORIANS** WHO HAD LAID WASTE TO **TIR NAN OG**.

YES... SLÁINE HAD COME A LONG WAY FROM HIS DAYS AS A FARM LABOURER, LAYABOUT AND THIEF...

AND, OF COURSE, HE OWED IT ALL TO HIS FAITHFUL DWARF AND COMPANION, **UKKO,** WHO HAD SO OFTEN KEPT HIM AWAY FROM CRIME, DEPRAVITY AND LOOSE LIVING...

AH, YES...AS I WRITE THESE WORDS HERE IN **THE ETERNAL FORTRESS,** CENTURIES LATER, I RECALL—AS IF IT WERE YESTERDAY—THAT GREAT BATTLE ON THE FROZEN SEA WITH **BALOR** AND HIS **DEMONS OF THE DEEP...**

THE NOISE AND THE TUMULT... THE CLASHING OF SWORDS AND AXES... THE SCREECHING OF HORNS AND BAGPIPES... THE SCREAMS OF THE WOUNDED...THE THUNDER OF CHARIOTS...THE TRUMPETING OF THE WAR-BEASTS...

AND THAT TERRIBLE MOMENT WHEN THE POWER OF THE MOST HOLY **WEAPONS OF THE EARTH GODDESS** WERE UNLEASHED...

THE **FLAMING SPEAR OF THE SUN** THAT WAS ALIVE AND THIRSTY FOR SLAUGHTER...

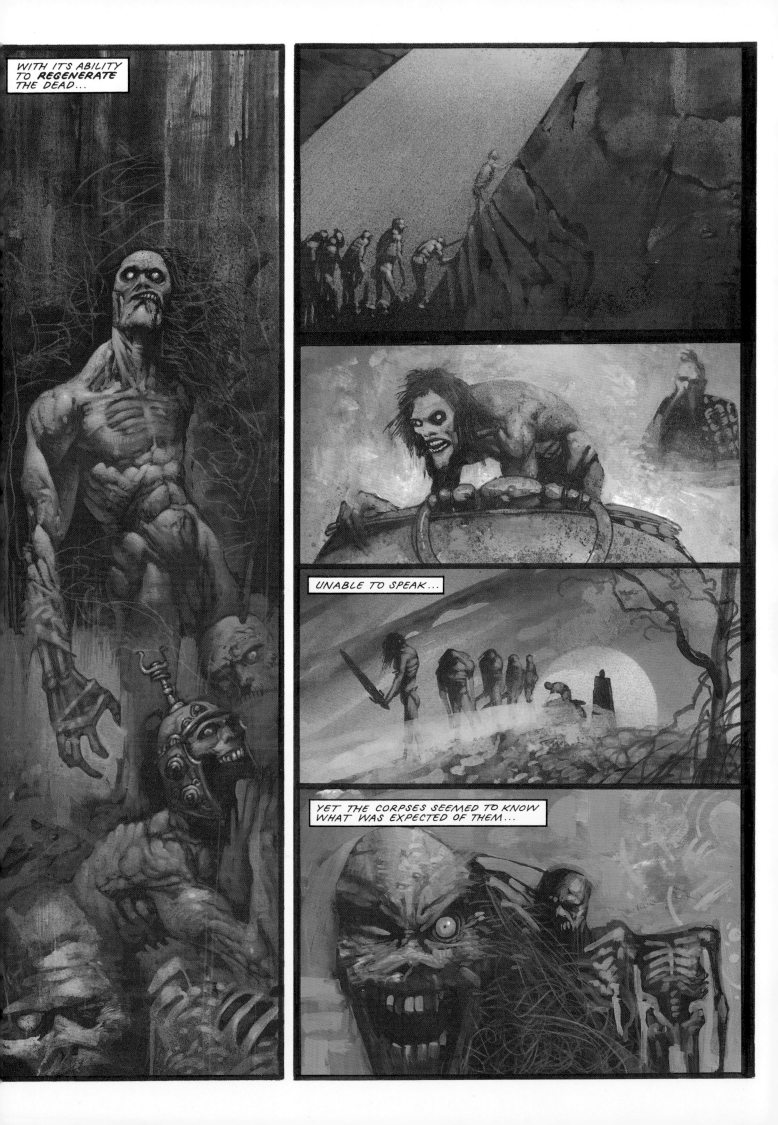

WITH ITS ABILITY TO **REGENERATE** THE DEAD...

UNABLE TO SPEAK...

YET THE CORPSES SEEMED TO KNOW WHAT WAS EXPECTED OF THEM...

LURCHING BACK ONTO THE BATTLEFIELD, THE "HALF-DEAD" WENT ABOUT THEIR GHASTLY WORK...

...KEEN TO SEND THE SEA-DEMONS TO THE PLACE THEY HAD JUST VISITED.

WHETHER IT WAS THE **VIBRATIONS** FROM THE BATTLE: THE THUNDER OF CHARIOTS...

THE CURSES...

...AND SCREAMS OF THE DYING...

THE WARM BLOOD SPILLING ON THE ICE...

THE CORPSES PILING UP ON IT...

...OR THE LONG AWAITED THAW...

SOTH!

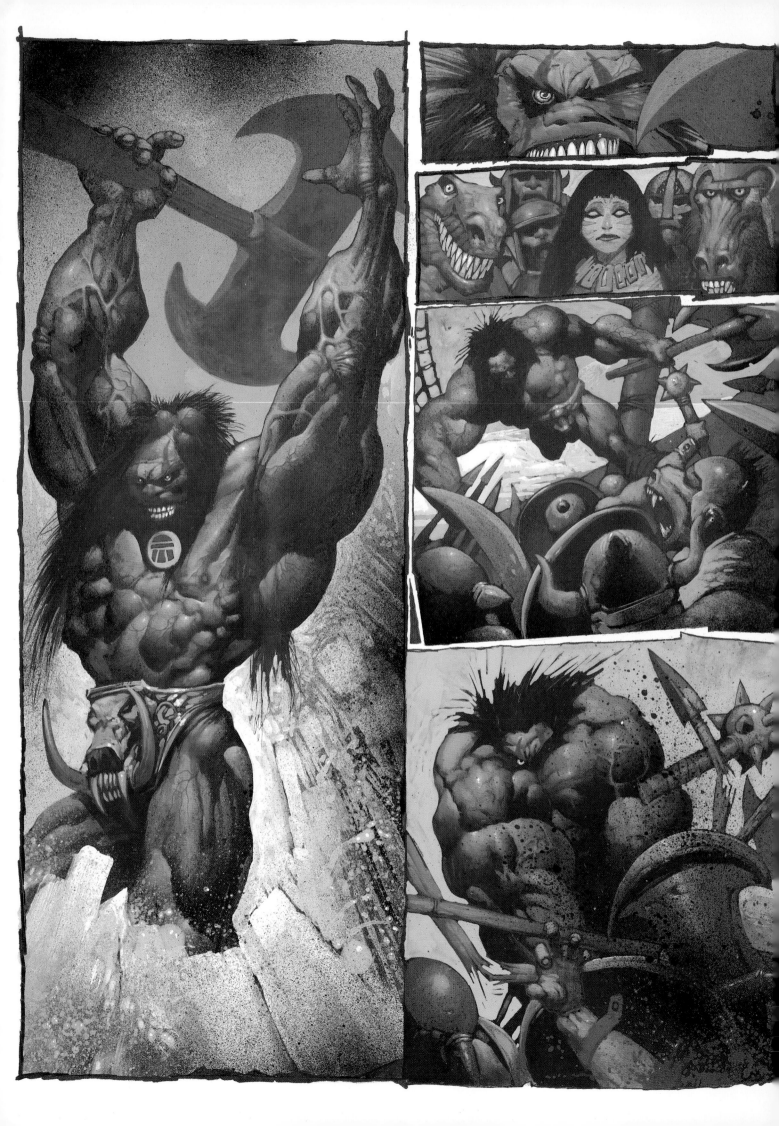

LEAPING OFF THE YACHT, TOTALLY WARPED, SLÁINE BEGAN A MURDEROUS, CRIMSON, BRUTAL CHARGE, HEWING AND CLEAVING, STABBING AND CUTTING AND MUTILATING HIS WAY THROUGH THE DEMONS...

KILLING FIFTY TO THE LEFT... AND FIFTY TO THE RIGHT. HE DIDN'T THINK IT TOO MANY.

(IN FACT, IT WAS ABOUT AVERAGE FOR SLÁINE.)

"INFLICT PUNISHMENT ON THE SKULL SWORDS..."

"PLAY HURLEY WITH THEIR HEADS."

BUT SLÁINE'S ARMY WAS DECIMATED BY HIS BATTLE WITH THE SEA DEMONS...

AND THE DRUNES WERE EQUIPPED WITH *SKY SHIPS* FROM WHICH THEY BOMBARDED HIS FORCES...

H'MM... I DON'T RECALL THE BEARD THE LAST TIME I SAW HIM... THE AGEING PROCESS MUST BE ACCELERATING.

YES... DESPITE HIS ENTHUSIASM FOR HIS SUBJECT, HE'S DETERIORATING FAST.

HOW LONG HAS HE GOT?

A FEW DAYS BEFORE HIS MIND GOES... A WEEK, PERHAPS, BEFORE THE END. THAT'S WHY I'VE BEEN PUSHING HIM TO COMPLETE THE SAGA.

QUITE SO...

...JUST AS LONG AS HE CAN REACH THE POINT WHERE SLÁINE DIES.

CHEERFUL THE WORK!

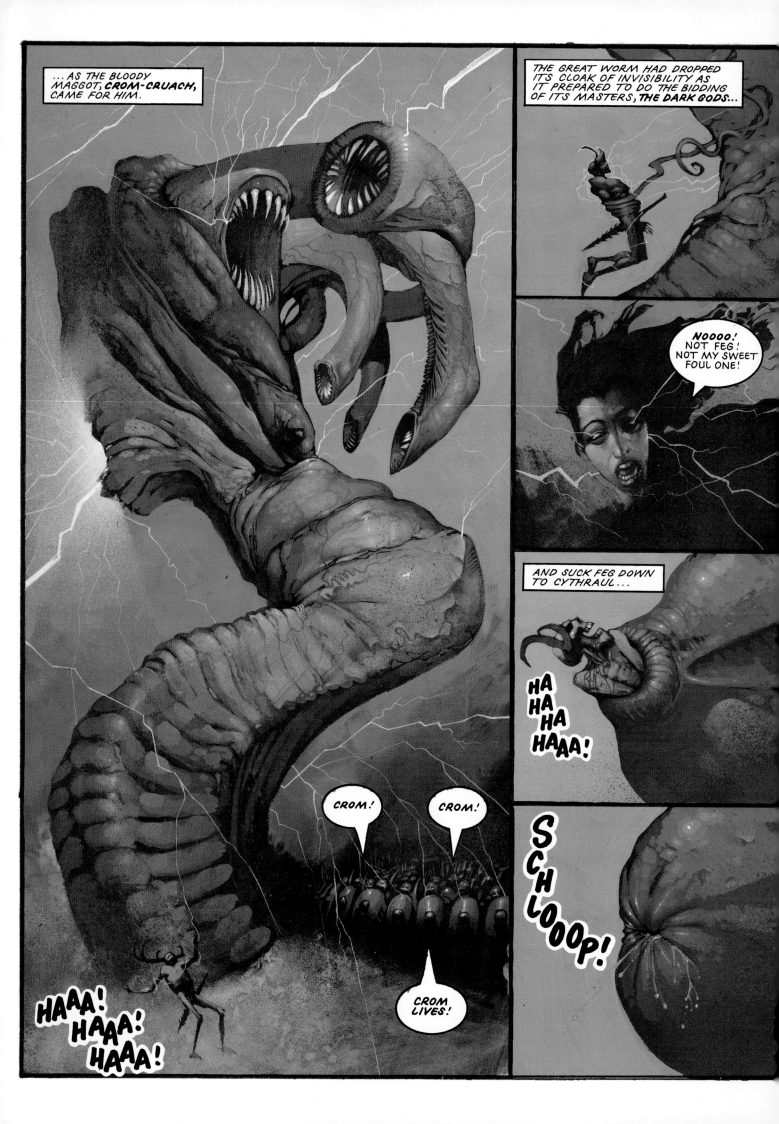

FOR **MEDB**, WHO WORSHIPPED THE DESTRUCTIVE SIDE OF NATURE, IT WAS TIME TO CALL ON HER GODDESS...

HEAR ME, **WHITE GODDESS OF DEATH**, MY SISTER! GRANT ME YOUR FAVOURS OF TERROR, PAIN AND DESTRUCTION. GIVE THEM TO THESE WARRIORS THAT NEED YOUR CRUEL TOUCH SO DEARLY!

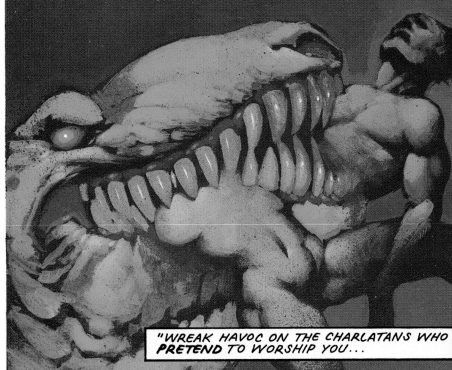

"WREAK HAVOC ON THE CHARLATANS WHO **PRETEND** TO WORSHIP YOU...

"OPEN THEIR WOUNDS... WEAKEN THEIR SWORD ARMS... TERRORISE THEIR HEARTS...

"SOIL THEIR BREECHES!"

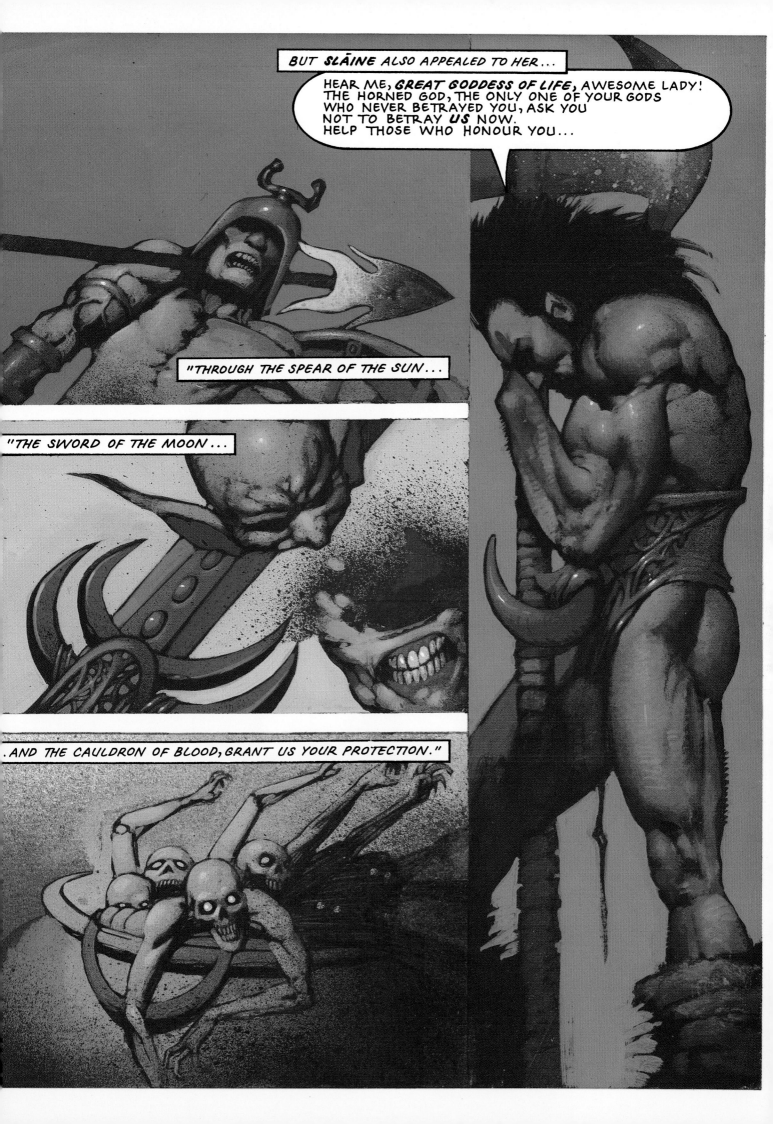

TRIPLE GODDESS, MAIDEN, WOMAN AND HAG, YOUR STRONG HORNED CONSORT, YOUR SON AND YOUR LOVER, HE WHO IS SOMETIMES LAUGHING, SOMETIMES GRIM, CALLS UPON YOU TO AID US.

A-AARGH

I AM NOT AFRAID OF DEATH, BECAUSE I KNOW NOT TO TAKE LIFE TOO SERIOUSLY. IT'S ALL A *GAME* TO YOU. IT'S YOUR *SPORT.*

I'M THE LAUGHTER IN THE WOODS... *REMEMBER?*

BUT YOU'RE HAVING SO MUCH *FUN* HERE...

WHY END IT SO SOON?

THEN SLÁINE RECITED MYSTERIOUS WORDS GIVEN TO HIM BY THE EVER LIVING ONES.

SATOR AREPO TENET OPERA ROTAS

IT WAS A *LOVERS CHARM* THAT IT'S SAID NO WOMAN CAN RESIST... (THE WORDS CURIOUSLY ARRANGED SO—WHEN WRITTEN DOWN—THEY ALSO READ FROM RIGHT TO LEFT AND UP OR DOWN.)

WHATEVER THE SPELL'S MEANING, IT HAD THE DESIRED EFFECT... FOR THE NAVAL OF DANU GLOWED WITH POWER...

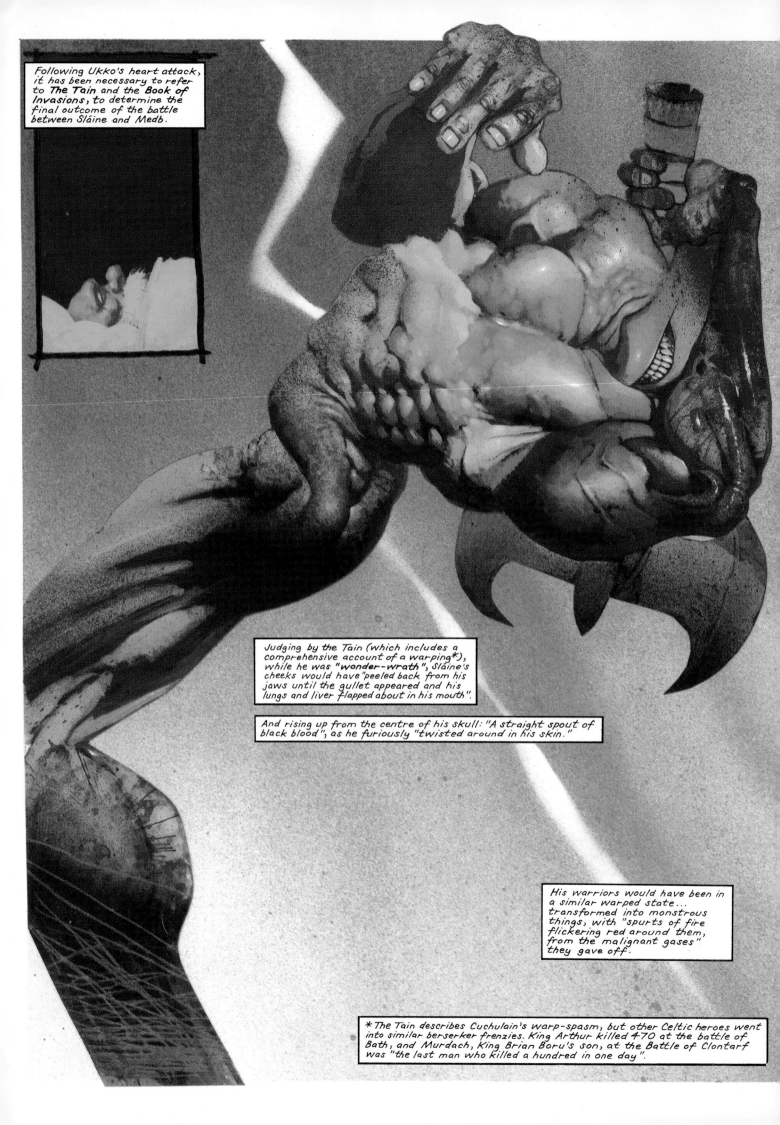

Following Ukko's heart attack, it has been necessary to refer to *The Tain* and the *Book of Invasions*, to determine the final outcome of the battle between Sláine and Medb.

Judging by the Tain (which includes a comprehensive account of a warping*), while he was "**wonder-wrath**", Sláine's cheeks would have "peeled back from his jaws until the gullet appeared and his lungs and liver flapped about in his mouth".

And rising up from the centre of his skull: "A straight spout of black blood", as he furiously "twisted around in his skin."

His warriors would have been in a similar warped state... transformed into monstrous things, with "spurts of fire flickering red around them, from the malignant gases" they gave off.

*The Tain describes Cuchulain's warp-spasm, but other Celtic heroes went into similar berserker frenzies. King Arthur killed 470 at the battle of Bath, and Murdach, King Brian Boru's son, at the Battle of Clontarf was "the last man who killed a hundred in one day".

Nevertheless, it would seem likely Medb was defeated—although Ukko does not indicate whether she survived the battle or shared the fate of her spectral army.

Neither does he make it clear whether she is the sensual Queen Medb of legend who had "at least nine husbands" and became ruler of Connacht.

But she is, at least, a kindred spirit of the legendary character, described as being "lavish with her physical friendship", who is reputed to be buried in the Hill of Kings, in Sligo

As to the Tribes of the Earth Goddess, the Annals state they were, "Most notable Magicians who did wonderful things by magick and other diabolical arts, wherein they are exceedingly well skilled."

And relate how their flying ships crossed the Irish coast concealed in a black cloud, "which cast a darkness upon the sun for three days and nights..."

"It was in a mist the Tuatha de Danaan, the Tribes of the Goddess Danu, the Men of the Triple Goddess, came through the high air to Ireland.

"It was from the North they came; from four cities skilled in Witchcraft and Wizardry: great Falias and shining Gorias and Finias and rich Murias...

"And they brought from those four cities their four most holy and precious treasures: A Stone of Virtue from Falias they called the Lia Fail, the Stone of Destiny...

"And from Gorias they brought a Sword from whose stroke no one ever escaped or recovered...

"And from Finias a Spear of Victory that was alive and thirsty for slaughter...

"And from Murias the fourth treasure, the Cauldron that no company ever went away from unsatisfied."

HIS SEVEN-YEAR REIGN HAD COME TO AN END AT LAST AND IT WAS TIME TO BE REUNITED WITH THE GODDESS IN DEATH...

COVERED IN GREENERY AND MADE DRUNK WITH MEAD SO HE WOULD FEEL NO PAIN, HE WAS TIED IN THE "FIVE-FOLD BOND" — ONE THONG FOR EACH TRIBE.

AFTER BEING BEATEN TILL HE FAINTED, HE WAS FLAYED, BLINDED, SORELY WOUNDED AND IMPALED WITH A SPEAR OF MISTLETOE...

... CUT UP INTO JOINTS AND ROASTED OVER A SACRED FIRE AS DRUIDESSES DANCED AND SANG...

THEN DISTRIBUTED TO HIS PEOPLE...

"TASTE THE FRUITS OF THE FOREST. EAT OF THE GOLDEN BOUGH. DRINK OF ITS SAP, SO YOU MAY BE VIGOROUS AND FRUITFUL."

AND THAT WAS HOW **KING GANN** DIED... **KING SENGANN** WAS LEFT TO WANDER IN HAPPY VALLEY, A WOOD SLÁINE SET ASIDE FOR THE MOON-TORN... NOTHING VERY INTERESTING HAPPENED TO **KING GENANN**... AS FOR **KING RUDRAIGE**, YOU WILL RECALL **NIAMH** HAD ONLY AGREED TO AN ANNUAL MARRIAGE. NOW THAT YEAR WAS OVER, SHE WAS FREE TO MARRY SLÁINE...

...BUT ONLY FOR A YEAR ALSO. AFTER MY CHILDHOOD AS A POSSESSION OF A KING, I DON'T INTEND TO LET ANYONE OWN ME AGAIN.

YOU WON'T REGRET IT, NIAMH. I SWEAR THIS TIME I SHALL BE FAITHFUL.

I HAVE NO FEAR ON THAT SCORE, SLÁINE. YOU KNOW THE OLD SAYING: MEN HAVE GOATS' EYES WHEN CHOOSING THEIR WOMEN...

...BUT WOMAN HAVE GOATS' EYES IN KEEPING THEIR HUSBANDS TO THEMSELVES.

HOW TRUE. HOW TRUE. AND WHAT ABOUT **RUDRAIGE**..? AN AMICABLE SEPARATION, WAS IT, DEAR..?

OH, YES...

"...HE HAS FOUND COMPANIONSHIP ELSEWHERE."

I'M SO GLAD. BECAUSE DIVORCES CAN BE SO MESSY. BUT NATURALLY YOU'LL NEED SOMEONE TO HANDLE **THE LEGAL SIDE** — TO ENSURE EVERYTHING IS DIVIDED PROPERLY. AND, AS ONE DWARF HELPING ANOTHER, I'D ONLY BE TOO PLEASED TO OFFER MY SERVICES. AT VERY REASONABLE RATES...

SILENCE, DWARF!

AND SO MY SAGA DRAWS TO A CLOSE.

ALTHOUGH THERE IS MORE TO TELL.

HOW THE KINGDOM OF PLEASURE FARED... HOW MEDB'S GRIM PROPHECY CAME TRUE... THE CIRCUMSTANCES OF SLÁINE'S DEATH... AND MY OWN MOST FORTUNATE ESCAPE...AND THE **INSIDIOUS NEW EVIL** HE WOULD FACE...

YES, SOME WOULD SAY HIS **GREATEST ADVENTURE** WAS YET TO COME. AND IT IS I WHO MUST TELL IT, FOR IT IS I WHO CAN. I, **UKKO THE DWARF,** WHO WAS HIS FRIEND AND COMPANION IN THE DARK AND TERRIBLE DAYS THAT LAY AHEAD.

IN A TIME WHERE THERE IS NO TIME, IN A PLACE WHICH IS NOT A PLACE, I WRITE.
OF A ONCE GREAT KING, SLÁINE MAC ROTH, WHO RULED AN EMPIRE THAT WAS NOT AN EMPIRE, IN A PAST WHICH IS NOT THE PAST, OR THE FUTURE, BUT FOREVER.
BECAUSE LEGENDS ARE ETERNAL.

"Five Chieftains, who were at the same time brothers, landed in Ireland. They found it uninhabited and divided it in five equal proportions amongst themselves.

"When these five brothers, namely Gann, Genann, Sengann, Rudraige and Sláine had divided the island, each portion had a little section meeting at a certain stone in Meath said to be the Navel of Ireland, as it were, placed right in the middle of the land.

"As time went on and fortune varied and, as is her want, turned many things upside down in a short time, Sláine became the High King of the whole of Ireland.

"As a result Sláine is called the first King of Ireland."
Ancient Chronicle

The End

Afterword

Sláine – The final quotation which describes how Sláine became the first King of Ireland is taken from Gerald of Wales' book *The History and Topography of Ireland*, written in the twelfth century. The same account is given in the medieval *Book of Invasions* which also describes how Sláine's tribe landed in Ireland at Inber Sláine – the mouth of the River Slaney. Other place names testify to the memory of a once mighty king – Baile Shlaine the town of Sláine and the Hill of Slane close by where he is reputed to be buried. The hill was also the site of a magical contest between Druids and St. Patrick.

Tribes of the Earth Goddess – Fir Bolg (Men of Lightning or Men of the Belly) was the name sometimes given to Sláine's tribal confederacy. In the *Book of Invasions*, the Tribes of the Earth Goddess were a separate warring group who arrived in Ireland thirty years later. In our saga the two invasions have been merged together.

Although Sláine is not intended as an exact reconstruction of Celtic myths purists should note that both tribes would have been Goddess worshippers and the second invasion is generally regarded as an artificial one. The details of it were probably adapted from the first invasion (*Early Irish History and Mythology* by T.F. O'Rahilly, Dublin, p. 141).

The Stone of Destiny – Near the Hill of Slane is Tara, ancient seat of the High Kings of Ireland. A pillar stone on the hillcrest is reputed to be the Stone of Destiny. In the churchyard is another version with an engraving on it said to be the Horned God.

Crom-Cruach – The 'Bloody Maggot' God was worshiped on the Plain of Adoration where 'great was the horror and scare of him.' An ancient poem tells us:

Here used to be
A High Idol with Many Fights
Which was named the Crom Cruach
It made every tribe to be without peace

He was their God
The withered Crom with many mists
The people whom he shook over every host
The Everlasting Kingdom they shall not have

They did evil
They beat their palms, they pounded their bodies
Wailing to the demon who enslaved them
They shed falling showers of tears

Death of a King – In traditional societies the King was ritually killed at the end of his reign. In one instance in Malabar when the ruler's twelve year term of office was at an end it was customary for him to stand up before the cheering crowd and generously slit his own throat.

The Dark Goddess – the concept of an all powerful Goddess, constantly changing, is an unfamiliar one in this age of male Gods. It is best summed up in *The White Goddess* which quotes Samuel Taylor Coleridge's Rime of the Ancient Mariner as the definitive description of her:

Her lips were red, her looks were free,
Her locks were yellow as gold,
Her skin was white as leprosy,
The Nightmare Life-in-Death was she,
Who thicks man's blood with cold.

Main Sources – Theory of the Grail as a return to the womb - *Women of the Celts* by J Markale, Inner Traditions International; The Horned God as a role model – *The Horned God* by John Rowan, Routledge and Kegan Paul; The Horned God's relationship with the Goddess – T. Skinner; The Goddess as Supreme Deity – *The White Goddess* by Robert Graves, Faber and Faber.